Grandmother's
KITCHEN
WISDOM
LIBRARY

NATURAL REMEDIES & NUTRITION

BY

DR. MYLES H. BADER

MORE USABLE FOOD INFORMATION THAN ANY BOOK EVER
PUBLISHED

THE ULTIMATE CHEFS GUIDE TO FOOD SECRETS

NATURAL REMEDIES & NUTRITION
BY
DR. MYLES H. BADER

Published by:
Creative Product Concepts, Inc.
1435 Walnut Street
Philadelphia, PA 19102

Distributed by:
Creative Product Concepts, Inc.
1435 Walnut Street
Philadelphia, PA 19102

Printed in the United States of America
First Printing May 2002

ISBN: 1-929199-10-4

Grandmother's
NATURAL REMEDIES & NUTRITION

We've all heard the expression, "Grandmother knew best."

My Grandmother was the kind of woman that always had a pot of coffee on the stove, something wonderful smelling in the oven, and the answer for any questions I could dream up. Nothing threw Grandma. "I've lived through some tough times," she use to say to me, "It'll take more than a cough or two to keep me down." Whenever I got sick, Grandma always had "Just the thing" that would make me feel better. Like her mother and grandmother before her, my Grandma had a host of home remedies that could cure whatever ailed you. Unfortunately, these invaluable pieces of homespun advice were rarely written down.

This book is about grandmother's home remedies. Not just those used by my grandmother, but those handed down from generation-to-generation in families everywhere. Many of the remedies used in this book originate from Native American culture. Many may remind you of your own grandmother. Others will be new to you, but may soon become part of the legacy you pass on to your family.

My Grandmother and the women like her relied on common items that were grown in their herb garden, kept in their cupboard, or bought at the general store. Often, the closest doctors were miles away – a distance that was longer still before the invention of the automobile. So, back when Grandma was a girl, they would turn to home remedies the way we would turn to our neighborhood pharmacy. In this book, you'll find tried and true natural alternatives to help many common illnesses. The remedies use everyday items, herbs and foods that are easily obtainable.

It's important to note that the remedies do not take the place of our physician or prescribed medication, but are provided as another source of information regarding a number of illnesses and how they were treated before modern medicine came of age. Many of the remedies have been very successful and all are without side effects when used as recommended.

As you leaf through this book, I hope that some of Grandma's spirit comes through. I also hope that you will be reminded of your own grandmother and great-grandmother who have passed on a precious oral tradition that needs to be cherished. My hope is that this book will help you to continue their legacy.

TABLE OF CONTENTS

CHAPTER 1

TOUCHY SUBJECTS

The skin consists of three layers and is the largest organ of the body. It tends to act as a shield between eh body and the thousands of foreign substances that can damage the body. Our environment contains pollutants that could harm and even kill us if they were allowed to gain entry. The skin reacts to these harmful elements by erupting, flaking, scaling, itching, redness, color changes, cracking and dryness.

CLEAR UP YOUR COMPLEXION: ACNE

This common skin condition occurs when the sebaceous glands, which lie just beneath the skin and produce the natural oils that keep the skin lubricated, become clogged or are not regenerated in sufficient quantity to handle the load. This may result in whiteheads or blackheads being formed. Pimples are then formed when the bacteria is released from these clogged pores.

For serious blemishes, try washing with Fels-Naptha soap, strong stuff for oily skin. However, if your skin is normal or dry, you'll need something gentler for your face.

Clearing Up The Outside From The Inside

Grandma, like mothers everywhere, swears that all the high-fat food we love so much does a number on our complexions. Scientists may not be quite as convinced, but to be on the safe side, avoid chocolate, chips and fried foods.

Eating more brown rice is good advice for improving overall health. It is also good for your complexion. To ward off pimples and other facial blemishes, make brown rice a regular part of your diet.

Keeping the skin and body hydrated by drinking at least eight glasses of water daily is an effective method of keeping the skin clear and assisting it in clearing wastes.

Studies show that zinc deficiency may contribute to acne. Be sure to check with your doctor before taking a supplement, since too much zinc may have harmful side-effects.

Spread It On Thick

To help fight pimples, use a paste of onion and honey. Cook one sliced onion in a half cup honey until it is tender. Mash with a fork to form into a paste and allow the mixture to cool. Apply to the problem area, leaving it on for an hour before rinsing away with warm water. Use this treatment every night before going to bed until your complexion is clear and sparkling. An application of egg whites helps distribute the skin's natural oils more evenly, eliminating both dry and oily patches. Swab the egg white on your face with a cotton ball, allow to stand for five minutes and remove. Studies have shown that certain amino acids in the egg white's protein may have some anti-inflammatory properties. In most cases, small blemishes and pimples can be eliminated or reduced in size in a matter of days.

Oatmeal has long been used to control the spread of acne, as well as to speed up the healing process. Prepare the oatmeal as directed (without the milk, brown sugar, and raisins, of course!) and apply to the face. Let it stand for ten to fifteen minutes before washing off. The abrasive action of the oats cleanses deeply and increases the peripheral circulation in the affected area, which speeds up healing.

Acne and eczema as well as psoriasis have responded well to a paste made from the grain amaranth and placed on the affected area. Internally, it is taken as a tea. Take two teaspoons of the fresh seeds and cover them with boiling water, simmer on low heat for five to six minutes, remove from the heat and add two to three amaranth leaves and allow to steep for thirty to forty minutes. Two cups per day should provide relief from a number of skin problems.

Make An Astringent At Home

Blackheads respond well to lemon juice, a substance with wonderful astringent properties. Rub lemon juice over the blemished skin before going to bed and rinse with cool water in the morning. After a couple of days, you should see definite results.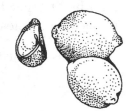

Vinegar is a mild acid and cleans the affected area, reducing bacterial levels. Apply apple cider vinegar with a cotton swab and allow to stand for ten minutes before removing with a mild soap.

You'll find cucumber toners in most expensive lines of skin care products. Cucumber extract soothes skin and helps dry out acne. Juice a cucumber and apply it to your blemishes with a cotton ball. After fifteen minutes, rinse your face.

Erasing The Past

If you had a serious problem with acne in the past, you probably still have scars from it. To fade them, apply a paste consisting of one teaspoon honey mixed with a teaspoon of nutmeg. Rinse it off after twenty minutes, using cool water. Repeat this procedure twice a week. You should notice a difference within a couple ofmonths.

Out, Out Damned Spots

In our teen years, we discovered that our grandmother had a real pet peeve about pillowcases. She blamed many common skin irritations and blemishes on dirty pillowcases, and insisted that we change them every week without fail. She reasoned that when you spend six to eight hours rubbing your face on a piece of cloth, you are bound to clear off dead skin and other residue that may contain bacteria. This idea also reinforced one of Grandma's favorite expressions: "Cleanliness is next to Godliness."

STOP HIDING THOSE HANDS: AGE SPOTS

Age spots are areas of increased pigmentation in the skin, caused either by aging or excessive sunlight exposure. They are generally harmless. However, if they change color or cause discomfort, you should consult a physician immediately. As Grandma use to say: "An ounce of prevention is worth a pound of cure." Take care of your skin by using a sunscreen with an SPF factor of at least fifteen when going outside. Aloe vera preparations can slow down the appearance of these spots as you age.

Taking a zinc supplement may help fade age spots. However, consult your physician before trying this remedy, since high doses of zinc may have harmful side-effects.

Rub It In To Rub Them Out

Mix onion juice with twice the amount of vinegar and rub into the age spots twice a day. The brown patches should disappear before your very eyes.

Vitamin E oil is highly beneficial to the skin. It can promote healing of cuts, prevent or fade scars, and relieve dry skin. It also appears to help fade age spots. Before you go to bed, rub some Vitamin E oil into the brown patches and let it work overnight. You should see a noticeable difference in a few weeks.

Lemon juice can be used as a temporary measure to bleach out age spots. Dab a small amount on the spot and allow it to dry. For the best results, this should be repeated at least two to three times each day. It may take two to three months before you see results.

Give It Some Time

Apply buttermilk compresses to the area for twenty minutes twice each day. The mild lactic acid found in milk products appears to be the active ingredient. Due to individual differences in skin, treatment time may vary.

The herb gota kola has been used for hundreds of years for memory problems. It also works on age spots. Mix a solution of a quarter teaspoon powdered gota kola, a half cup very hot water and an eighth teaspoon Korean ginseng. Place a poultice on the areas and let stand ten minutes. Apply twice a day. You should see results in about one month. Gota kola is an effective bleaching agent, but it may take longer than some of the other treatments.

Fountain Of Youth Food

Chick peas are a veritable fountain of youth. They are low in fat, high in fiber and nutrients, all of which will keep you feeling youthful and energetic. You can also use them to fade age spots. You can buy them dried or canned. If dried, prepare them according to the directions on the package. Mash up a small bowl of them and add enough water to make a paste. Rub the chickpeas over the brown places, letting it stay until it dries, and then wash your hands. If you keep doing this every day, your hands will start looking years younger.

THE BLACK AND BLUE BLUES: BRUISES

Bruising occurs when the skin is not broken, but the underlying tissues are injured. This results in small blood vessels being broken, causing localized pain, swelling, and a black-and-blue area.

Tea And C

Drink twelve ounces of orange juice a day. Vitamin C strengthens the walls of the blood vessels. Taking a Vitamin C supplement of 500-1,000 milligrams a day will also work wonders for repeated bruising.

Severe bruises involving broken blood vessels and skin discoloration respond well to the herb ledum. Take as a tea or apply externally to the affected area.

Fade Away

Apply an icepack to a bruise or immerse the affected area in cold water to reduce swelling and fade black-and-blue marks more quickly. Do not place ice directly on skin or use water that is painfully cold. This remedy is effective because it constricts blood vessels and there is less bleeding beneath the skin.

Gently apply witch hazel to the bruised area to speed up healing and help the mark fade. Witch hazel also constricts blood vessels to lessen bleeding. Natural witch hazel may be more effective than commercial preparations. Boil one teaspoon powdered leaves or twigs in a cup of water, strain, and cool. Apply the ointment to the bruised area.

Don't Knock It Til You Try It

Apply a poultice of grated turnip to a bruise to promote faster healing. Leave it in place for up to half an hour.

Boil a small amount of comfrey leaves for ten minutes, and let cool. Soak the bruised area in the mixture or apply as a poultice.

Carefully apply a salve of parsley and a teaspoon of butter to a bruise. It should soothe the sore area and help fade the black-and-blue mark.

Keep It From Coloring

To prevent a bruised area from discoloring, try any of these three remedies. Right after you bump into the end table or knock your leg against the car door, head for your kitchen and break out the sugar. With moistened fingers, gently rub the sugar across the injured area. The next day, you should wake up without any trace of black or blue. You can also prevent a bruise by applying an arrowroot paste, a couple of tablespoons of arrowroot and a little water, to the skin. It will dry up and fall off, leaving behind unblemished skin. When you get a bruise, eat a banana and rub the skin with the inside of the peel. To completely ward off a bruise, secure the peel to the injured area and leave overnight. By morning, there should be no bruise to speak of.

Don't-Drink-Me Tea

Try this Italian cure for a nasty bruise that helps relieve pain and swelling. Brew a tea from one large tablespoon of oregano and a cup of boiling water. Let it set for ten minutes and strain. Put the wet oregano in a piece of cloth and apply to the bruise. Keep the liquid to refresh the oregano leaves.

How To Sweeten Up A Bruise

Grandma kept a huge jar of blackstrap molasses in her kitchen, but it wasn't with her baking supplies. She kept it in the cupboard with the other ingredients for her home remedies. Whenever I'd come home from school all black and blue from horsing around, she'd tear off a piece of brown paper and dip it in the molasses. She'd secure it to the bruise with a bandage, and several hours later when she took it off, the bruise would be almost completely gone.

TOO CLOSE TO THE FLAME: BURNS

There are three different degrees of burns. First degree burns, the least serious, are identified by redness only, second degree by redness and blistering, and the most serious, third degree burns by the destruction of the skin and underlying muscle. Third degree burns need a physician's care as soon as possible to avoid serious infection.

If Grandma could get to the store, she'd pick up some over-the-counter remedies that helped relieve the pain of burns. Many of these commercial preparations contain active ingredients to deaden pain, as well as ingredients to fight infection. Many also contain aloe vera which is soothing to burned skin.

Sweet Relief

Sometimes when my grandmother was baking, she would burn herself taking a pie out of the oven. Whenever that happened, she'd take a small piece of pie crust dough rolled thin and put in on the burn, leaving it until it dried up. By the time it fell off, the pain from the burn would be completely gone.

For a sweet burn cure, apply honey to the affected area to ease pain. Since bacteria will not grow on honey, it also promotes quick healing and prevents infection. Some people feel that the honey is more effective if combined with sauerkraut or comfrey root.

Layers of apple butter can help heal a burn. Spread apple butter over the affected area and keep reapplying as each coat dries. Keep this up for a day or two, and the burn should be well on its way to healing.

Swell Advice

Place a cold compress on the affected area to reduce swelling and pain. The burned area should be elevated to reduce swelling.

Quick Relief

Apply aloe vera to first degree burns immediately, and to second and third degree burns after healing has begun.

If you're outside and need an immediate treatment for a burn, apply mud to the area to cool the skin.

A burned tongue can really hurt. For a severe problem, wash your mouth out with cool water until it starts to feel better. You may also want to try a few drops of vanilla extract to ease the pain.

When burned by hot wax, tar, or melted plastic, use ice water to harden the material before trying to remove it.

Don't Eat Your Vegetables

Apply layers of sliced raw potatoes to the burn, refreshing every few minutes. The starch in the potatoes will form a protective coating of starch to soothe the skin. You can also use a piece of fresh pumpkin or onion.

You can use items out of the refrigerator, mushrooms and radishes, to soothe a burn. Slice a mushroom and put the pieces on your burned skin to promote healing. You can use the radishes to make a poultice for the burn. Make sure that they are cold, straight out of the refrigerator. Puree in a blender and apply to the burn.

The Carrot Juice Cure

Grandma had an unusual treatment for a burn or a scald. She would immediately soak the affected area in ice water and then place a dressing dipped in pure carrot juice on the area. She repeated this three to four times a day for about three days.

Grandma's Open Cupboard Cures

Try the vinegar and brown paper bag cure for a burn. Soak a piece of brown bag in white cider vinegar. Placing it on the affected area should have a cooling effect and relieve the pain.

Applying baking soda mixed with extra virgin olive oil to first and second degree burns will promote healing and reduce the chances of scarring.

Vitamin E oil helps skin heal more quickly and prevents scarring and blistering. Apply liberally to the area several times a day and bandage with sterile gauze. This vitamin's anti-oxidant properties may help reduce inflammation.

Vanilla extract relieves the pain of a grease burn.

Place a piece of charcoal on a burn and leave it for at least an hour. The pain will quickly subside. When you take away the charcoal, much of the redness should have disappeared.

Comfort From Within

Once a burn has started to heal, make a strong tea from blackberry leaves and apply on a compress two to three times a day to speed healing.

To relieve the discomfort of second and third degree burns, increase the low-fat protein in your diet to at least 3,000-4,000 calories a day. Drink at least eight to ten glasses of water a day.

SMOOTHING THE ROUGH SPOTS: CORNS AND CALLUSES

Calluses are formed when the body tries to protect itself from a severe irritation by building up excess hard protective tissues that are usually flat. Corns are formed as a result of pressure which forces the body to build up raised layers of skin, causing pain.

You're Soaking In It

Give your feet a soothing bath in oatmeal water. Add a little less than two cups of oats to five quarts boiling water. Boil down to four quarts of liquid, remove from heat, and strain, retaining the liquid. Soak your feet for twenty minutes or more.

A good warm soak, plain water or with a variety of ingredients, will help tired feet feel better and can reduce discomfort from corns and calluses. Try adding a little vinegar, iodine, Epsom salts, or baking soda to the water for added effectiveness.

Stop It Before It Starts

Grandma preferred to prevent a problem whenever she could. She didn't have much patience with fancy shoes that didn't fit right and caused foot problems. Comfort, comfort, comfort, that was her motto. She particularly recommended avoiding high heels and shoes with pointy toes.

Callus And Corn Coverage

Dissolve six crushed aspirin in one tablespoon of water. Apply to the corn or callous to treat it. Don't use this remedy if you are allergic to aspirin.

Soak one crumbled piece of bread in a quarter cup of vinegar, letting it stand for thirty minutes. Apply to the corn as a poultice and tape in place. Leave it on overnight, and by morning, the corn should easily come off. If it doesn't, repeat the remedy several times, until the corn falls off.

Tape a piece of pineapple peel to your corn, with the flesh-side against your skin. Replace every day until the corn is gone.

There is nothing nicer than a hot cup of tea, and you can recycle the used tea bag as a remedy for your corns. After your morning cup of tea, secure the tea bag to your corn and leave for half an hour. Keep doing this every day until the corn disappears in a week or two.

Getting Ready For Bed

Every night before going to bed, rub some vitamin E oil, available at your local health food store, into the corn or callus, massaging for a couple of minutes. Let your feet air day for a few minutes before putting on a pair of socks and turning in for the night. After a couple of nights of this treatment, a corn should fall off and a callous should be softened.

Cut a small piece of lemon and secure it to the corn, pulling on a pair of socks to keep it in place overnight. Keep doing this until the corn is gone.

Soak an onion in some white vinegar. Before going to bed, tape a piece of the onion onto the corn. By the time you wake up in the morning, you should be able to remove the corn. If it proves to be stubborn, repeat the process and try again the next morning.

If a corn or callus is really bothering you, apply lemon juice or vinegar as a poultice and leave overnight. It will help soften the spot, so you can remove dead skin.

FAREWELL TO FLAKES: DANDRUFF

Dandruff is caused by scalp glands that do not function properly, causing drying and then scaling of the skin. Itching and burning may occur in serious cases, and a physician should be consulted before any treatment at home.

In some cases, exposure to sunlight will help. Also try consuming one serving of yogurt a day for a week.

Nothing Flaky About This Cure

Grandmother's favorite method of getting rid of dandruff was her special scalp massage. Mix one cup apple cider vinegar in one cup of water and add ten mint leaves. Bring this mixture to a boil for five minutes, then allow to stand at room temperature for twelve hours. 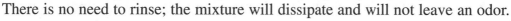 Strain and massage into the scalp twice each day for seven days. There is no need to rinse; the mixture will dissipate and will not leave an odor.

Wash Those Flakes Right Out Of Your Hair

A shampoo of the herb bay laurel eliminates dandruff. Prepare the solution with one quart boiling water and three to four teaspoons of crushed bay laurel leaves. Allow to steep for thirty minutes, strain and allow to stand in the refrigerator for one hour. After you wash your hair with your normal shampoo, massage some of the tea into your scalp. Repeat the treatment a second time and allow it stay on your scalp for one hour before rinsing. The herbal shampoo needs to be used regularly for the best results.

Try a lemon rinse to banish dandruff. Apply the juice of half a large lemon to your hair, wash your hair with your regular shampoo, and rinse. Mix the other half of the juice with two cups of water, and rinse again. Continue using this lemony rinse every other day until you are without flakes.

Shampoo your hair as you usually would and rinse with chive tea. To make the brew, let a tablespoon of chives steep in a cup of boiling water for twenty minutes. If you follow this treatment once a week, it should fight off your dandruff problem.

Thyme For A Cure

Grandma would brew up a batch of thyme rinse to treat dandruff. Boil four table-spoons of dried thyme, using two cups of water, for ten minutes. Strain and cool. Use half of the mixture to rinse damp hair making sure it gets to the scalp, and keep the other half for another time.

A derivative of thyme oil is an active ingredient in Lysterine. If you'd rather go to the drug store than the health food store, pick up some Lysterine and massage into the wet scalp with a cotton ball, waiting an hour or so before washing your hair. Repeating several times a week for a couple of weeks should clear up the dandruff.

Here's The Rub

Grandma always recommended that we massage our scalp to keep the skin healthy. She often turned to the items sitting on her kitchen shelf as home remedies. For dandruff, wash your hair, massage in a little warm olive oil, wrap your head with a towel, and leave overnight. In the morning, brush your hair to loosen dandruff flakes, and rinse out the oil. One of the causes of dandruff is a dry scalp, and an occasional warm oil treatment will remedy that in a jiffy. You don't want to over-do, however, since too much oil can make the problem worse.

One way to relieve your dry scalp without making your hair oily is to use this mas-sage and soak method. Pour out enough peanut oil to massage into your entire scalp and warm it up before applying. Rinse with lemon juice and let both ingre-dients work for fifteen minutes before shampooing with baby shampoo. You can use corn oil in much the same way.

FLAKY, SCALY, ITCHY: DERMATITIS

Dermatitis is an allergic reaction that causes flaking, scaling and itching of the skin. Metals are frequently the cause, but creams, ointments, and certain plants may also be the culprit. Dermatitis tends to spread and may become a serious problem.

Apply a mixture of the herb goldenseal and vitamin E with a small amount of honey to add consistency. Leave on the affected area for twenty to thirty minutes and use at least three times a day.

HOW TO BE A SMOOTHIE: DRY SKIN

Nature's Healing Hand

A traditional Hawaiian remedy for dry skin is kukui nut oil. It's great for both face and body. The oil is pleasant-smelling and absorbs quickly, without a heavy, greasy feeling.

For dry skin care, try cleaning your face in whole milk. Add 1 teaspoon of castor oil to three tablespoons of warm milk. Shake well to mix and apply to your face with a cotton ball. This milk and oil mixture is terrific for removing makeup and dirt.

Dry skin may be alleviated by using a chamomile and lavender preparation.

Over-The-Counter Curatives

For chronic dry skin, try Eucerin, an over-the-counter product that contains mineral oil and lanolin, ingredients that help your skin retain moisture.

The farm hands at Grandma's stumbled on a great treatment for dry skin, Bag Balm, a product that helps soothe a mother cow who is nursing. It's especially good for the stubborn, dry skin on the bottom of the feet. Apply it thoroughly before bedtime and put on socks to keep it from getting on the sheets. You can use Vaseline in the same way, on the tough skin of elbows, knees and feet. Take a bath before bed, apply the jelly to your feet, and pull on socks.

Petroleum jelly is also an effective facial moisturizer. Glob some of the petroleum jelly on your fingertips and rub on your face and neck. Keep adding water to continually thin the layer of jelly on your face until it no longer feels greasy.

Nutrition Solution

Sulfur, found in onions, garlic, asparagus, and eggs, tends to keep the skin smooth with a youthful appearance.

Another Reason To Quit

Smoking dries out skin and causes premature wrinkling around the mouth.

PAMPER YOUR FACE FRESH: FACIAL MASKS

Facials are a wonderful idea for skin health and beauty. It's best to apply facials in the evening, when your skin will be free of makeup for several hours. Facial masks are most effective after a shower or bath, after your face has been gently steamed and the pores are open. Always start with a clean face and neck and rub the mixtures in with an upward circular motion.

The Banana Mask

This is an excellent mask for dry skin. It's also recommended to reduce and prevent fine lines and wrinkles. Mash a ripe banana with a drop or two of peanut oil. Spread it on your face and neck and leave on for about a half an hour. Remove with lukewarm water. You may apply this mask every day or every other day to promote softer skin.

The Cocoa Powder Mask

Cocoa powder may be a popular baking ingredient but it also makes one of the best masks for a dry skin problem. Prepare a mixture of two cups cocoa powder, two tablespoons dairy cream, and one to two tablespoons extra virgin olive oil. The consistency may have to be worked with and the ingredients altered slightly until you have a thick paste, one that won't fall off too easily once applied. The olive oil will prevent the mixture from drying out prematurely. The mixture is approximately twenty-five to thirty percent linoleic acid which is the ingredient that will do the job. The reason grandma's skin always looked great was this inexpensive solution. She never had the money to purchase all those fancy skin preparations.

The Eggplant Yogurt Mask

This is a fine mask for oily skin. Blend a quarter of a small eggplant with its skin and one cup of plain yogurt in a blender. Spread over your face, being careful to avoid the delicate skin around your eyes. Leave on for twenty minutes then rinse with lukewarm water. You might want to finish this treatment off with an astringent or toner. Keep chamomile tea in a spray bottle in your refrigerator and spritz the tea on your face after you rinse off the mask, or use anytime as a quick skin refresher.

The Egg White Wrinkle Mask

This mask is said to smooth the wrinkles associated with age. You can apply this mask three or four times a week. Mix an egg white with some sweet cream. Lightly spread around your eye area and let it set for half an hour to an hour. Rinse with lukewarm water.

The Honey Mask

Apply unheated honey to your face with your fingertips. Spread with an upward circular motion. Rinse with lukewarm water after twenty minutes. This sticky mask should aid in ridding your complexion of blackheads and blemishes. You'll feel refreshed.

The Honey And Cream Mask

This is another good mask that has a good reputation for helping wrinkles. Mix one teaspoon of honey with two tablespoons of heavy whipping cream. Mix very well. With your fingertips, gently massage the mixture into the fine lines and wrinkles on your face. Leave on for at least half an hour. You'll feel a gentle tightening. When you've had enough, rinse off with lukewarm water. I've heard that people have made this a part of their evening ritual and many swear by the results. You be the judge.

The Oatmeal Cleansing Mask

In a blender, place one cup of uncooked oatmeal and blend until it's reduced to a powder. Mix the powder with one egg white, a half cup of skim milk and three drops of almond oil. Spread the mask on your face and neck—avoiding the tender area around your eyes. Leave on for half an hour before rinsing with lukewarm water.

The Oily Oatmeal Mask

Add vegetable oil to cooked oatmeal—just enough to make it easy to spread. Massage into your face and neck. After half an hour, wash off with lukewarm water. If used daily, this mask may reduce wrinkles.

The Papaya Mask

You'll need a blender for this one. Peel a ripe papaya and puree. Spread the pureed fruit on your face and leave on for twenty minutes. Rinse with lukewarm water. This refreshing mask will help remove dead skin cells.

The Too-Much Sun Mask

This mask is not for sunburns, rather, it's for skin that has been enduring years of sun abuse—the kind often called "leathery." Mix two tablespoons of flour into two tablespoons of raw honey. Add about three tablespoons of milk—enough to make the mixture the consistency of toothpaste. Smooth the paste on your face and neck with your fingertips, avoiding the delicate area around your eyes. Leave on for twenty minutes and rinse off with lukewarm water. Pat dry. Follow with a toner and moisturizer.

THE NASTY SIDE OF NATURE: POISON IVY AND POISON OAK

When bare skin comes in contact with the sap of the poison ivy or oak plant, it develops redness, rash, blistering and swelling in susceptible individuals. Scratching makes the problem worse and may transmit it to other parts of the body. Animals that come into contact with the plant can transmit the sap to humans.

Cleaning Up

Wash the affected area with alcohol immediately to lessen the rash. Combine the juice of two limes in one quart water mixed with equal parts white oak bark tea. This solution should be applied with a wet cloth or bandage and changed when it dries out. It should reduce healing time and severity of the attack.

Soap is a wonderful remedy for taking care of poison ivy or oak—before the rash appears. After contact with the plants, be sure to scrub the exposed area with soap to wash off the resin. Getting the resin off your skin is important—it will keep you from breaking out in a rash. Thoroughly washing the area within one to two hours of exposure should alleviate the problem before it starts. Any kind of soap should work fine, but some people swear by a brand called Fels-Naptha. I recommend scrubbing with this soap before going into an area where the plants are known to be, then scrubbing again after you return.

Some people find that household bleach helps to remove poison ivy or oak resin. First, wash the area well with a soap like Fels-Naptha. Then, soak a cotton ball in a half water, half bleach mixture and dab it on the area. Do this three times the first day that you notice blisters and you should see a definite improvement. Bleach can be a skin irritant, so test a small area before you proceed.

Herb Help

The herb goldenseal has been reported to relieve symptoms in just a few hours and even cure the rash in a day. Make a paste or purchase the liquid form for the fastest results.

Here's a hot idea that MUST be used cold. During the summertime, when poison ivy poses the biggest problem, make a batch of mugwort tea and keep it in a jar or bottle in the refrigerator until needed. As soon as you realize you've come in contact with the poison ivy, grab the refrigerated tea and wash your skin with it. If applied soon enough after the contact, mugwort tea can rid your skin of the rash-causing oil—but only if the tea is cold. Hot tea will open your pores and make the rash worse.

Friendly Foods

If poison ivy or oak is driving you bananas—this is the perfect cure for you. Peel a banana and set aside the fruit. You'll only need the peel for this remedy. Rub the inside of the skin on your rash every hour for one whole day. Use a new banana peel for each application. If you're lucky, someone you know will have a banana bread recipe as good as my Grandma's.

Placing tofu directly on a poison ivy rash can stop the itching and feel very cooling and soothing. Keep tofu in place with gauze pads.

Oatmeal is a great remedy for all kinds of itchy skin ailments, but it's especially good on poison ivy and poison oak. Fill some fine netting (or a sock or old pantyhose) with oatmeal and put it in a bathtub that's filling with warm, not hot, water. Hot water will make the rash worse. Have a good long soak. For even more itch control, leave the oatmeal residue on a little while before rinsing off. For patches of poison ivy or oak, make a paste out of oatmeal and tepid water. Place it on the rash until the itching subsides.

Getting Muddy

If you're camping or away from home, try putting fresh mud on the poison ivy or oak. The mud will help to draw out the infection.

TOO MUCH OF A GOOD THING: SUNBURN

Excessive exposure of the bare skin to ultraviolet light for a prolonged period leads to burning.

Taking The Sting Out

Take the heat out of a sunburn quickly by applying apple cider vinegar to the burn. Put the vinegar in water to dilute it (try one part vinegar to two or three parts cool water) and apply it to the areas that are burned. That hot feeling you get from too much sun should disappear and the stinging sensation will subside. You may even find that applying the vinegar solution will keep you from peeling.

Cold clay poultices are very effective. Green tea that has been cooled and placed on the affected area with a washcloth will also have a soothing effect. The poultice should be left on for about thirty minutes every few hours.

Another soothing sunburn remedy is a cold milk compress. Put equal parts of milk and ice in a quart container and add about two tablespoons of salt. Soak a washcloth in the milky mixture and place it on the raw area. Leave the washcloth on for up to fifteen minutes and repeat three or four times during the day.

For a sunburned face, try spreading on yogurt or sour cream. Leave on for twenty minutes and let the yogurt or sour cream take the heat out of your burn. Rinse with lukewarm water.

Buttering Us Up

When one of us kids would come home "glowing like a firefly" from a nasty sunburn, Grandma would grab one of her handy kitchen helpers: butter. She would use the freshly churned variety. You may find that a can of evaporated milk will also do the trick. Milk has been known to ease a sunburn, but be sure to use whole milk. It's the fat content in the liquid that makes the raw skin feel better.

Don't Forget To Moisturize

Aloe vera gel does wonders for relieving the pain of sunburns and helps moisturize the skin. Many of today's commercial brands of sun care products claim aloe vera as one of the ingredients. If you have an aloe vera plant at home, cut off a leaf, break it open and spread the gel right on your burn. It's soothing and lubricating and helps in healing so you'll feel better in no time. If you don't have a plant handy, you can purchase aloe vera gel at your local health food store.

Another soothing solution for sunburns is vitamin E capsules. But in the case of a burn, you don't swallow it, you cut it open and spread the oil on the tender area. The oil will ease the pain of a sunburn and will also lubricate your skin to guard against peeling and blistering.

Grandma's Secret Anti-Wrinkle Lotion

My grandmother's skin always looked great. She hardly wrinkled despite her advancing years. Whenever anyone asked about her complexion, she would say, "Clean living is my secret." One day I saw her preparing a lotion from avocados, and she swore me to secrecy. It was the oil that was her secret. It makes one of the best suntan lotions. Avocado oil will also keep the skin in excellent condition and slow the skin's aging process.

Rub-A-Dub-Dub

Try taking a baking soda bath to relieve the pain of a sunburn. Sprinkle about a cup of baking soda into lukewarm water (careful, not too hot!) and soak for fifteen to twenty minutes. You might want to follow this up with one of the topical remedies.

Another bath additive good for sunburn pain is colloidal oatmeal. Look for colloidal oatmeal at you pharmacy or sundry store.

How about a milk bath to take the heat and sting away? Empty a package of powdered nonfat dry milk or a quart of low-fat milk into a tub of warm water. A half an hour soak should soothe away the sunburn pain.

The Eyes Have It

The delicate skin around the eye is very susceptible to sunburns. Tea bags are a good remedy for sunburned eyelids. Cool wet tea bags placed on the eyes will feel great and help in healing. Tea is also soothing for other sunburned skin. Try brewing a pot of strong tea, let it cool, and apply it on sunburned legs, arms, backs, etc.

Here's another eye-easing remedy. Prepare a poultice made from grated apples and place on your eyelids. Then lie back and relax—it will be helpful if you can keep the poultice on for about an hour.

Another good poultice for sunburned eyes is made by lightly beating one egg white. Wrap the poultice over your closed eyes and get a good night's sleep. Remove the poultice when you wake up and you should feel a noticeable improvement.

FROG PRINTS: WARTS

These are clusters of cauliflower-like growths that may appear anywhere on the body and are usually caused by a virus. They are contagious and should be isolated with a bandage and never irritated or picked.

Simple Medicine

Another remedy for warts is aspirin. But you don't swallow it. Instead, dip your hand in warm water and place a damp aspirin tablet on the wart. Cover it with a Band-Aid or a gauze pad with tape to keep it in place. Put the aspirin on before going to bed. That one application should do the trick. Your wart should be history in just a few days. This remedy is not recommended for those who are allergic to aspirin.

Putting iodine on a wart several times a day can help to dissolve it away. Although this remedy may take a while, keep applying the iodine several times a day and the wart should fall off within a few weeks.

Here is a cure for plantar warts—the warts that appear on the soles of the feet. These warts can spread, so don't pick at them. Rub castor oil on the plantar wart each night before you go to bed. Keep this up until the wart's all gone.

Salt is also used as a cure for warts. Moisten some table salt and place it on the wart covering it with a Band-Aid. Keep this treatment up until the wart disappears.

Kitchen Cures

One of Grandma's remedies for warts was to strap on some blackstrap molasses. Apply a poultice of the molasses and keep on as long as you can. She would also feed us a tablespoon of the blackstrap molasses each day. After about two weeks of the molasses treatment, the wart should drop right off.

Go figure—placing a crushed, fresh fig on the wart for a half hour each day will cause it to disappear. Be sure the fig is very mushy.

Try putting a used tea bag on the wart for fifteen minutes every day. Your wart should be toast in a week and a half.

Here's an egg cure—sort of. Soak your hand in the water from hard boiled eggs. Do this for ten minutes a day until the wart disappears. For some reason, this remedy works specifically for warts that appear on the hands.

Place crushed fresh garlic directly on the wart and cover with a dressing for a 24-hour period. The wart should develop a blister and eventually fall off. Castor oil has also been used with varied success.

Meadow-cine

Picking dandelions can have positive healing effects on warts. Break the dandelion off at the stem—a white, milky substance will appear. Put this on the wart several times a day until the wart goes away. Be careful, though. Dandelions may cause a rash for people with sensitive skin.

TURN BACK THE CLOCK: WRINKLES

The herb cleavers has been used as a facial cleanser and skin tightener with excellent results. It far outshadows most of the over-the-counter preparations that cost a small fortune. To prepare a mixture, bring one quart of pure filtered water to a boil. After removing the water from the heat, add three to four tablespoons of cleavers herb, then cover the mixture and allow it to steep for forty-five minutes. Apply the mixture by lightly saturating a small towel and placing it over your face for ten minutes three to four times a day for four days. The effects will remain for three to four weeks and will become evident in about two weeks.

CHAPTER 2

BED-RIDDEN BLUES

STUCK WITH THE SNIFFLES: COLDS

Colds are caused by a virus, and the symptoms include various kinds of upper respiratory discomfort. Mucous should be allowed to flow freely, since the body rids itself of infection this way. The cold virus may take many forms making it difficult to fight.

A Few Tips On Prevention

"An ounce of prevention is worth a pound of cure." That was my grandmother's sage advice. Grandma recommended eating certain foods to help ward off colds and flus, and in fact, modern science has confirmed that there are benefits to eating more broccoli, parsley, and apples. The old adage that an apple a day keeps the doctor away may well be true! Grandma also recommended drinking raw sauerkraut juice every day to keep cold germs away. It has the added benefit of keeping you regular.

If someone at work has been coughing on you or one of your children has come down with a cold or the flu, take a cinnamon oil preventative immediately. Add five drops of cinnamon oil to a tablespoon of water and drink it down. Repeat three times a day. You can also take a teaspoon of eucalyptus oil to ward off a cold. Hold it in your mouth ten minutes before swallowing.

The shiitake mushroom has an important place in traditional Asian medicine. If you feel a cold coming on, add these tasty mushrooms to your favorite dish. Or you can take shiitake mushroom capsules if you prefer.

Tea And Sympathy

Grandma always said that when you've got the sniffles, something warm to drink and few soothing words went a long way to help the patient recover. Here are a few soothing suggestions:

Several herbal teas have a significant effect on cold symptoms. Goldenseal tea stands out as one of the best and is known to contain antibiotic properties.

Make a tea with cayenne pepper, just a pinch if you're not used to hot food. It can help prevent a cold or speed relief. The capsaicin in the pepper helps to loosen mucous.

Try this congestion curing tea. Make a mullein tea with two teaspoons dried leaves in one cup boiling water, steeping for ten minutes. The herb mullein can be found in health food stores. It helps soothe sore throats and breaks up mucous, easing congestion.

A tea made with slices of fresh ginger root or powdered ginger will help break up mucous and reduce fever. It may also boost the immune system.

Try this very-citrus cure that allows you to use your favorite liquor. In a saucepan, combine the juice of one orange, one lemon, and one grapefruit, along with a tablespoon of honey. Be sure to stir it while you bring it to a boil. Add an ounce or so of brandy or whatever you have on hand and enjoy.

Don't Knock Chicken Soup

Chicken soup works wonders. Heating the soup releases a chemical that relieves some of the symptoms, especially nasal drainage. Other foods that may also help are garlic, onions and hot peppers.

Drink a broth made from potato peels one to two times a day. The peels should be approximately a half inch thick and should include the skin. Clean the skin thoroughly with a good organic cleaner and a vegetable brush. Boil for twenty to thirty minutes with two stalks of celery. Cool and drink.

Don't Forget To Flush

Drinking a lot of water can help flush toxins and germs out of the body. You can also re-hydrate with unsweetened fruit juices and various kinds of herbal teas, including the ones mentioned here.

Rub It In And Breathe Deeply

Rub oil of eucalyptus into your chest two to three times a day. Breathing in this oil clears up congestion and opens airways. You can also place seven to eight drops of eucalyptus oil in hot bath water or six to seven drops in a cup of boiling water. Place a towel over your head and inhale the vapors.

If you have a chest cold, try rubbing a salve made from one raw egg white and four teaspoons prepared mustard into the chest. Apply a hot compress to the chest on top of the mixture and keep reapplying as the compresses get cold, four or five times. After the last one, wash off the salve and turn in for the night, making sure you don't get a draft. You should be able to sleep better and feel a lot less congested in the morning.

To clear out chest congestion, heat a cup of white wine and inhale the vapors.

Grandma's Hot Dog Helper

Grandma used to say that the best way to lick a cold was a good old-fashioned "mustard plaster." She claimed this could cure almost any symptom. It is still used in many rural areas of the United States and Canada. To make the plaster, mash the leaves and stems of a fresh mustard plant into a thick pulp. Before applying the plaster, cover the chest with a thin layer of Vaseline. Put on the plaster and cover with a cloth or towel, taping it down. It is essential to protect skin with the Vaseline against any adverse effects of the mustard, such as blisters. For the best results, the plaster should be left on overnight. When grandma used the plaster, she would always make sure to tuck us in real good. By placing pillows on either side of us, she made sure we didn't move around too much during the night, keeping us "snug as a bug in a rug."

Smelly Solutions

Garlic appears to contain a substance that fights infections of all kinds: bacteria, viruses and fung-uses. It can help ward off or cure a cold. Fresh garlic is most effective, but you can also take dried garlic in the form of capsules or tablets.

Onions, like garlic, have traditionally been used to fight colds. If you're not an onion fan, look for onion preparations at your health food store.

A "Hard" Cure for Your Cold

Grandpa kept a flash of whiskey in the pie safe in the hallway. "Just for medicinal purposes," he always assured us. In fact, several traditional remedies for the common cold involve alcohol. Brew a mug of very strong black tea, add one tablespoon honey, one tablespoon cognac, one quarter teaspoon cinnamon, and one teaspoon butter. The tea should be as hot as you can stand. You should wake up the next morning with soggy sheets, having sweat out the cold during the night.

If you prefer rum to cognac, try this remedy that combines the juice of one lemon and three teaspoons of honey with four teaspoons of rum. Before you go to bed, add the mixture to a glass of hot water and drink it down. You should feel much better in the morning.

Hot And Cold Cures

Soak in a hot tub that has ginger powder added to it, just before turning in for the night. Stay in the bath about fifteen minutes to get the full benefit. Make sure you dry off well afterwards to keep from getting chilled and dress warmly for bed. The ginger should help you sweat and rid the system of toxins. If the ginger does its job, you may have to change into a fresh, dry pair of pajamas during the night. By morning, you should feel noticeably better.

In traditional Chinese medicine, acupressure points are stimulated to relieve cold symptoms and cure the infection. Put a cube of ice on the bottom of each big toe, leaving in place until they melt. Do this three times a day until the cold clears up.

SOOTHING THE TICKLE: COUGHS

Soothing Solutions

Grandma's remedy for the common cough associated with a cold was hot tea with lemon and honey. The honey coats the throat and relieves the cough for a few hours. Another of her remedies was elderberry juice. Elderberry juice can calm the cough reflex for a long period of time. Fresh elderberries should be placed in a juicer with a slice of fresh lemon. Consume four to six ounces every three hours with a half teaspoon of honey or blackstrap molasses added as a sweetener.

Something Everyone Can Inhale

Put eucalyptus oil in a vaporizer and inhale the fumes.

Place ginger in very warm bath water. After the bath, wrap yourself in a terrycloth towel and sweat it out to loosen the mucous.

Peppermint, in its many forms, can be great for coughs. Put a drop of peppermint oil on your tongue to calm a coughing fit. Add a few drops of the oil to a cup of boiling water and inhale the vapors to relieve congestion. Make a tea of fresh peppermint leaves and drink with a little honey. You might even try a piece of peppermint candy. Grandma always had some in her purse, just in case.

If your congestion and cough is keeping you awake at night, take a warm bath before retiring, adding a couple of drops of pine oil to the water. The relaxing vapors should open up your bronchial passages and help you breathe more easily while you sleep.

Break It Up

Some hot spicy foods seem to help reduce the severity of a cough and break up the mucous and congestion usually associated with it. Try cayenne capsules, hot Chinese mustard and red horseradish. Apply hot onion packs to the chest and back at least three times a day. The onions should be sliced, steamed, and placed between soft cloths. Place a heating pad over the onion pack to help retain heat.

Control The Urge

Herbal cough drops help control the cough reflex. There are a number of effective herbs, such as eucalyptus and horehound.

Make a tea of slippery elm to get fast relief from a cough. You can buy lozenges with slippery elm as the active ingredient at your local health food store.

Throaty Solutions

A bay leaf poultice works wonders on chest congestion and coughing. Add twenty bay leaves to a cup of boiling water, cover and let stand for fifteen minutes. Put the warm, moist leaves in a cloth, placing it on your chest and covering with a towel to retain heat. Keep the liquid to re-freshen the bay leaves after an hour. Make sure you heat the water before soaking the leaves in it.

Gargle with a mixture of warm water and three tablespoons of dark Karo syrup. It will relieve a hacking cough.

Breakfast Breakthroughs

The fat in dairy products can help coat the throat and soothe a dry cough. Warm a cup of milk (not skim) and add two teaspoons of sweet butter. Drink two to three cups a day until the cough is gone. Milk contributes to the production of mucous, so you shouldn't try this remedy if you're coughing up phlegm or feel congested.

Certain ingredients in oatmeal can ease coughing. Make a thick oatmeal by following the directions on the package, reducing the water by a quarter cup. Flavor with honey to taste. Don't add milk to it, for the above reasons. Eat one cup of warm oatmeal, four times a day, or whenever the cough flares up.

A Honey Of A Cough Remedy

Grandma had a few "sweet" cures for a cough, involving honey. In the first, she combined six medium-sized onions, coarsely chopped, along with a half cup honey in the top of a double boiler. She simmered the mixture slowly for two hours and stored it in a tightly sealed jar. She'd warm it up and give the cough-sufferer a tablespoon every two to three hours. She made her other "sweet" cough cure from one teaspoon horseradish and two teaspoons of honey. She used the same dosage as her other honey remedy, one teaspoon every few hours.

Here's a tasty cough remedy you'll enjoy even when you're well. In a mug, combine the juice of a large lemon, two tablespoons of honey, three cloves, a half a cinnamon stick, and enough hot water to top off the cup. The steam will ease your congestion, and the lemony warmth will soothe your throat. Take a mug every three hours to relieve an irritating cough.

Use root vegetables and something sweet to stop a persistent cough. Cut the middle out of a rutabaga or yellow onion and fill with brown sugar or honey. Leave overnight and drink the juice in the morning. You can also take a beet and cut a hole in it. Add brown sugar or honey and bake until it's soft. It's a tasty way to knock out a cough. A turnip will also work.

Barley Makes It Better

Sometimes I dream about my grandmother's beef barley soup. That's how good it was. Although I have the recipe, it never tastes quite the same when I make it. Grandma was simply magic in the kitchen. When someone in the family had been hacking for a few days, she'd make a big pot of her soup and whip up a cough remedy while she was at it. She'd add the juice of one lemon to a cup of cooked barley and liquefy it. She'd give the cougher a cup of her barley brew, advising them to drink it slowly, every four hours.

Homemade Cough Syrups

Try these folksy recipes for cough syrup: Combine the juice of one lemon, a half cup olive oil, and one cup honey and cook for five minutes. Remove from heat and stir for several minutes. Take one teaspoon every two hours. Or mix a half cup water with a half cup apple cider vinegar, adding one teaspoon cayenne pepper and enough honey to sweeten for your individual taste. Take a tablespoon at bedtime and anytime you have a severe coughing fit.

For a dry cough, boil three unpeeled potatoes. Retain the warm water and sweeten with honey. Take a tablespoon whenever you feel a coughing fit coming on.

Get some fresh ginger root and cut off a small piece. Wash and chew on it, swallowing the juice. This should help soothe your throat and ease your cough. Ginger root is a little pungent for some people's taste. If it's too strong for you, try one of the other remedies.

Cure By The Cupful

A speedy cure for a bad cough is a warm cup of dill tea. Make the brew from one teaspoon of dill and a cup of boiled water. Let it stand for seven minutes before straining it. If you don't like the taste, sweeten it with a teaspoon or two of honey. Drink three cups throughout the day. If the cough isn't gone, repeat the next day, but you probably won't need to.

If you've had a cough so long it feels like you were born with it and you think you may have pulled a muscle in your back from all the endless hacking, it's time to take this powerful herbal remedy—fenugreek. On the first day, drink a cup of fenugreek tea every hour or so. Reduce the dosage the next day to four cups spread evenly throughout the day. You should be able to feel the chest congestion breaking up, and the cough should soon fade away. Since fenugreek is such strong medicine, only turn to this remedy when the others you've tried have failed and your cough is very persistent.

Licorice root has long been a staple in traditional healing. It is especially effective in treating upper respiratory ailments, including sore throats, colds, and coughing. Brew a tea from the licorice root or look for tea bags at your local health food store.

Grandma's Sunflower Cough Syrup

My grandmother often turned to her garden for her home remedies. Every year, she planted a row of beautiful sunflowers on one end of the garden, next to the peas, and at the end of the season, she would harvest the seeds and keep them on hand for snacks and cures. To treat a cough, she would whip up her Sunflower Cough Syrup. She'd cook a half cup of the seeds in five cups of water, boiling it down to about two cups of liquid. She'd strain out the seeds and add about a half cup of honey. She would get Grandpa's bottle out of the piesafe in the hall, whatever he happened to have on hand "for medicinal purposes," usually whiskey, and add some of that to her cough syrup, about three quarters cup as far as I could see. She would stir it all up and seal it tightly in a bottle. She would give the cough sufferer a teaspoon or two, four times a day. When you make this at home, you can use any hard liquor you happen to have on hand.

IT'S HOTTER THAN HECK IN HERE: FEVER

Normal body temperature ranges between 98 and 99 degrees Farenheight. If your fever is over 102 degrees Farenheight, you should consult a physician.

Fevers affect zinc absorption, so avoid supplements containing this mineral. Lobelia extract reduces fevers. Take a half teaspoon every three to four hours. If stomach discomfort occurs, reduce the dose to a quarter teaspoon.

Cool It

Fevers respond well to rubbing alcohol placed on the feet, palms and wrists. This increases evaporation through the skin and creates a cooling effect for the entire body.

Evaporation helps cool the blood. If you're running a fever, try taking a cool bath or shower, splash your face with cool water, or apply a cold compress to your forehead or wrists.

Out Of The Frying Pan

Heat can also cure a fever by inducing a therapeutic sweat. Take a hot bath or lie in bed under lots of warm quilts. Once you start perspiring, come out from under the blankets and let your sweat evaporate which will help cool the blood. Don't work out to cause sweating, and be sure to drink plenty of liquids.

Teas, in many varieties, have long been used to reduce fevers. The warmth will help induce a sweat. Brew a cup of black tea, add some sugar or honey, let cool for a minute, and slip in an ice cube. Sip slowly while resting in bed. Take a second cup if needed.

A Grape Idea

Try eating grapes throughout the day to relieve a fever. You can also drink pure, unsweetened grape juice, preferably diluted, always at room temperature, never chilled.

Put It On

For a homespun fever remedy, soak a folded piece of brown paper bag in white vinegar and place on the forehead.

Fry up some onions and put them in a bag or pillow case. Place it on the chest layered between towels and put a heating pad on top. This should cause sweating which will help break the fever. You can also put onion slices in your socks before bedtime, and the fever should be gone in the morning.

Drink It Up

Lemon balm has proven an effective fever remedy for Grandma and many other home healers. Steep leaves in boiling water to make a tea, and add lemon and honey. Two or three cups should help break a fever.

Grandma's "Fishy" Fever-Beater

Grandma swore by cod liver oil. The rest of us swore that it tasted really awful, so she tried to mix it with other things to help it go down more easily. Mix up a batch of Grandma's Fever Beater with two or three tablespoons of lemon juice, a half teaspoon cod liver oil, and honey to taste. Remember cod liver oil is strong tasting stuff, so go easy on it.

WHEN IT HURTS TO SWALLOW: SORE THROAT

This ailment may be caused by an environmental irritant or infection. It is a severe irritation of the mucous membrane at the back of the throat.

Here's a note about prevention: During the cold and flu season, it's important to be aware that germs can spread. Make sure to wipe telephones, door handles and other shared surfaces—even the television remote—with a disinfectant spray. You can also use Lysol Disinfectant Spray on pillowcases and bed linens to keep sick family members from re-infecting themselves.

Grandma's Works-Every-Time Tea

Grandmother had a great remedy for sore throats. This tea made from fresh hyssop works wonders. To prepare the tea, place two to three teaspoons of the dried herb in a cup of boiling water and allow to steep for ten to twelve minutes. Two or three cups a day should help relieve the problem.

Grandma's Gargles

Whenever I had a sore throat, my grandmother had me gargle with salt water. She would put about a teaspoon or two of salt water into lukewarm water and stir it up. I say about a teaspoon or two because when it came to measurements for cooking and baking, my grandmother's measuring technique was by sight, not science. She would hand me a glass of the salty water several times during the day and night, until I started feeling better.

Try gargling with a solution of a half teaspoon of sea salt with a small amount of chlorophyll added every hour. For that annoying feeling of post nasal drip, Grandma would use a vinegar and water gargle. She claimed that it cut the excess mucous in the back of the throat. Take about a tablespoon of apple cider vinegar in a glass of lukewarm distilled water and gargle. Sometimes, the vinegar would sting my throat. Then Grandma would use the honey and lemon remedy instead.

Another good gargle for a sore throat is hydrogen peroxide. Gargling with the solution three times a day should bring relief. I recommend mixing water with a three percent hydrogen peroxide solution and gargling about three times a day.

One way to get rid of laryngitis is an apple cider vinegar one-two punch. Mix two teaspoons of apple cider vinegar in one glass of lukewarm water. Gargle the first mouthful and spit it out, then swallow the next. Repeat this pattern until you've finished the glass. You can repeat this every hour. Many people have found they can be heard again after about seven doses. This remedy can also be good for sore throats, but you will probably only need to repeat this "vinegar gargle swallow" for two or three hours and you'll notice a difference.

Nothing To Sneeze At

This is a remedy that may sound strange, but give it a try. Put some cayenne pepper in ginger ale. This won't get high marks for flavor, but both the cayenne and the ginger have properties that will lubricate and heal the throat.

Sweet And Sour Solutions

Another of Grandmother's sore throat remedies was honey and lemon. Take a tablespoon of honey and squeeze some lemon on it (reconstituted lemon juice will do). Then, lean back and drizzle it down the back of your throat. I don't think this went a long way toward the healing of the sore throat, but it got rid of the persistent scratchy feeling long enough for me to fall asleep. And as far as remedies go, honey and lemon is very easy to take—especially for children.

A tea made from raw honey and lemon juice will help soothe the affected area. Honey is the only food that will not grow bacteria. Plus coating the throat with honey will reduce the level of bacterial growth and speed healing.

Tea You Don't Swallow

When you have a sore throat it is important to get lots of rest and drink lots of liquids (but make sure you don't drink any dairy). And while drinking herbal tea can help you feel much better, here's another way that chamomile tea can give you relief. Brew some chamomile tea and let it cool just enough for you to be able to handle the heat. Soak a white towel in it, wring it out and place it on your throat. Once the towel loses its heat, dip it in the tea again, wring it out and reapply.

Here's a tea you gargle with, but don't swallow. Steep three tea bags in a cup of boiling water—use the non-herbal kind—until the tea is very, very dark. Let cool slightly and gargle with the still hot beverage. Remember, don't swallow. Repeat this every hour until you begin to feel better.

Put The Hoarse Out To Pasture

Try this remedy for hoarseness. Slowly boil a half cup of anise seed in one cup of water for fifty minutes. Strain the anise seed, and while still hot add a quarter cup of raw honey and one tablespoon of cognac. Take one tablespoon every half an hour.

Grandma's Vampire Vapors

Here's a remedy that is wonderful for the throat but not so appealing to the nose: garlic. Grandma knew that garlic had a lot of wonderful properties, and whenever she felt "a tickle on the creep" she would reach for the garlic, saying that it cleared her sinuses and helped her throat. Grandma would either put a garlic clove in her mouth or rub garlic oil on her neck. Neither of these remedies is recommended if you're expecting company, but Grandma swore that her smelly solution did the trick.

SEE NO EVIL, HEAR NO EVIL, SMELL NO EVIL

CLEAR THE CANAL: EAR INFECTION

Ear infections cause pressure to increase in the outer or middle ear. The canal becomes inflamed and swelling occurs. It may cause a temporary loss of hearing in the affected ear. These infections are very painful for both adults and children. A physician should be consulted.

Warming Trends

Heat is one of the best soothers for an earache. Put a washcloth in a bowl of water and microwave for forty-five seconds. Hold it against your sore ear. Then direct the airflow from your blow dryer into your sore ear, keeping if far enough away so that your skin and hair don't get burned.

Fill a handkerchief or clean sock with a quarter cup table salt. Wrap a rubber band around it to make a ball and warm in the oven on low-heat. Lie down with the compress against your ear. The heat should bring relief from the pain. Some people claim this remedy works better if you add a quarter cup raw bran to the salt.

If your child has an ear ache, try the hug remedy. Put one hand over one ear and press the other into your chest. Your body's warmth will make the ache better.

Splish, Splash, Don't Do Anything Rash

Getting water in your ear while swimming or showering can be very annoying. If you have a problem with swimmer's ear, put a few drops of jojoba or mineral oil in your ears before diving in.

Stick It In Your Ear

There are a number of substances that can be placed in the ear to relieve pain. Buy garlic oil capsules at your local health store. Poke a hole in one of the capsules and let the oil drip into your ear. Seal the ear with a cotton ball. The pain should begin to diminish within half an hour. You can also try mixing together four drops of onion juice and one teaspoon warm olive oil. Place in the ears the same way as above, making sure to plug the ears with cotton. Apply three drops to each ear, in the morning and evening.

Alleviate pain by placing a few drops of warm olive oil in the ear along with a drop of tincture of lobelia. Children who live around smokers tend to have more frequent ear infections. This method should not be used before seeing a physician, since it will cause problems if the eardrum has been perforated.

If the idea of putting something into your ear canal makes you uncomfortable, try this remedy instead. Put some castor oil on a cotton ball and add a little black pepper. Place on the outside of the ear to relieve pain.

Grandma's Russian Remedy

My grandmother called this cure for an earache her Russian Remedy, since it involves vodka, something she only allowed into the house for medicinal purposes. I had a terrible time with earaches when I was little, as many children do. She'd get out her medicine dropper and the vodka, and gently put a couple of drops, no more than four, into my ear. I don't think it was ever longer than five minutes before my ear felt much better.

CHAPTER 3

WELL, SHUT MY MOUTH!

SLAYING THE DRAGON: BAD BREATH

Bad breath is usually caused by improper dental hygiene, digestive tract problems or smoking. It may be a sign of poor overall health.

Brush Away Bad Breath

Change your new tooth brush every two months to avoid bacteria buildup. Try brushing your teeth and tongue with myrrh at least twice a week.

Baking soda is a fine old standby to use in place of toothpaste. It is abrasive enough to clean and whiten the teeth, as well as to keep bad breath away.

Brushing your tongue is a must if you have a problem with bad breath. Bacteria remain in the small deep pores in the tongue and must be brushed out. Baking soda works well for tongue brushing.

Grandma's Breathalizer

If there was one thing Grandma wouldn't stand for, it was bad breath. She always had a remedy handy for those of us who didn't pass her approval. You never refused when she told you to wash out your mouth. Here's the recipe for her home-made mouthwash: Place ten tablespoons of fresh powdered cinnamon in one and a quarter cups of inexpensive vodka. Add sufficient water to dilute the alcohol to a fifty percent solution. Place the mixture in a jar and allow it to stand for two weeks. Seal the jar well and shake it twice a day, once in the morning and once at night. After two weeks, strain the mixture into a clean jar and store in a cool place. Grandma always kept hers in the bathroom. When you use the mixture just add a half teaspoon to four ounces of water and swish it around several times in your mouth. Don't swallow—or you may fail a different Breathalizer test!

Chew On This

Chewing a small amount of parsley will correct most breath problems. Peppermint also contains cleansing properties.

For millennia, people have been chewing cloves to sweeten their breath. Give it a try yourself. Could all those people have been wrong for all that time?

You know how much cleaner your mouth feels after chewing a piece of Big Red? For a natural breath sweetener without added sugar, chew on a cinnamon stick. Also try chewing anise seeds. You'll especially enjoy this breath freshener if you like the taste of licorice.

Beat Bad Breath With Good Nutrition

Since poor overall health and bad nutrition can contribute to breath problems, try adding more fruits and vegetables to your diet, especially apples, green leafy vegetables, and psyllium (an ingredient in laxatives like Metamucil).

The next time you go out for Italian food and come back with garlic breath, suck on a lemon. It also works for onion breath. Some people believe this cure works better if you put salt on the lemon.

A Cup Of Fresh Breath

My grandmother was a big coffee drinker, and she made the best coffee you can imagine. To get rid of onion breath, she prescribed a cup of strong, black coffee. For friends and neighbors who didn't drink coffee, she recommended eating an apple to counteract oniony bad breath. Now that I think of it, she would eat an apple to freshen coffee breath. Maybe Grandma would have skipped the coffee treatment and just eaten an apple in the first place if she hadn't enjoyed a good, warm cup so much.

SOOTHING THE SENSITIVE SMILE: BLEEDING GUMS

Cut a small strip of lemon peel and wrap it around your finger so the white rind faces out. Rub the white area on the sore gum for five minutes, two to three times a day. The bleeding should stop, and the gums should heal within a week. You should also consume two fresh oranges a day.

PUTTING OUT THE FIRE: BURNING MOUTH

A number of spices will react unfavorably with the mouth's delicate tissues, causing a painful burning hot sensation and even damage. One of the more common spices that causes this reaction is cayenne, found in a variety of peppers. Grandma had two cures for this problem and both seem to work equally well. To quench the fire, try drinking either whole milk or beer. The chemical that causes the hot bite is capsaicin which dissolves easily in either fat or alcohol.

LIP BOMB: COLD SORES

Cold sores are caused by the virus herpes simplex. They are contagious and may last three to four weeks.

Keep It From Forming

Taking the amino acid, L-lysine, as a supplement, can help heal a cold sore or prevent one from forming. It's a good preventive

measure for those who have a chronic problem, getting more than three cold sores a year. Take 2,000 to 3,000 milligrams a day to keep cold sores away and double the dosage if you feel one coming on. Grandma was a stickler for good nutrition, and you can add lysine to your diet by eating more dairy products, potatoes, and brewer's yeast.

Exposure to sunlight triggers some cold sores, so you should protect your lips with a sunscreen with SPF 15 whenever you go outside.

Taking several acidophilus capsules daily or eating two cups of yogurt with live bacteria a day can help prevent cold sores from forming. The active bacteria seem to boost the body's immune response and may also have anti-viral properties.

Take 400 milligrams of Vitamin C a day to help prevent cold sores. If you feel one coming on, take double the dose. Grandma drank a glass of orange juice every morning, and I never knew her to have a cold sore.

Whenever someone in her family got a cold sore, my grandmother insisted they get a new toothbrush as soon as the sore healed to prevent re-infection. If you feel a cold sore coming on, get rid of your toothbrush immediately. This may keep the sore from actually breaking out. Of course, since cold sores are very contagious, don't come into close physical contact with anybody who has one.

Kitchen Cures

Eat three to four servings of raw vegetables a day for the Vitamin B to facilitate healing and stimulate the immune system. Yogurt will help rebuild friendly bacteria. Take four cloves of fresh garlic a day as a natural antibiotic.

Soothing Salves

Aloe vera was one of Grandma's favorite remedies. She grew her own plant and used it on a wide range of complaints. When somebody in the family felt a cold sore coming on, she would break off a leaf and dab the juice on the area to get rid of it. You can also use a commercial aloe vera gel.

When Grandma could get to the pharmacy, she had Mr. Simpson, our family pharmacist, mix up a solution of spirits of camphor. Dabbing a little on the sore with a cotton ball will help soothe the pain and dry it up.

While at the drugstore, my grandmother would also pick up some petroleum jelly. Placing the jelly on a cold sore can keep it from cracking, bleeding, and spreading.

Apply Vitamin E oil to a cold sore three times a day to get rid of it in a hurry. By the end of the first day, it shouldn't hurt anymore. By the next evening, it should be completely gone.

Make a paste of three tablespoons honey and one tablespoon apple cider vinegar. Place the paste on the sore three times a day to speed healing.

A salve of walnuts and cocoa butter can dry up a cold sore and relieve the pain. Combine a few ground walnuts with a teaspoon of cocoa butter. You'll be rid of the sore in a matter of days.

If you have a cold sore, make yourself a cold drink with plenty of ice. Move the ice on and off your cold sore to reduce pain and inflammation.

Overheard At The Local Bar

The red wine remedy can relieve cold sore pain and dry it up, as well. Put half a teaspoon of red wine in a bowl and leave it there for several hours. When you come back, much of the liquid will have evaporated. Apply what remains to the cold sore for quick pain relief.

CHOPPER WATCH: DENTURE PROBLEMS

A Perfect Fit

Dentures can be very annoying, even painful, if they are not relined at regular intervals or if they do not fit properly.

Massage gums that are sore from dentures. This increases circulation and decreases sensitivity. However, if you need to use this remedy often, you should have your dentures checked. They probably don't fit properly.

The Old Standby

Grandma's old remedies are just as effective as many new fangled ones. Baking soda is still at the top of the list. It cleans and deodorizes dentures. Stubborn stains should respond to household bleach, but make sure to rinse the dentures thoroughly before wearing them.

Soothing Salt Rinse

Rinsing with warm salty water has a soothing effect since the salt draws fluid from the tissues and reduces swelling. The mixture should be eight ounces of warm water to one and a half tablespoons salt.

BEATING BACK BACTERIA: PLAQUE

Grandma had her own way of removing dental plaque. She recommended drinking two cups of black tea daily to inhibit the growth of plaque forming bacteria from decaying foods. Recently, this was proven by researchers from Washington University.

THE ROOT OF THE PROBLEM: TOOTHACHE

Dab Away The Pain

Grandmother's remedy for a toothache was to place a small amount of oil of cloves on the affected tooth. There is a chemical in cloves that soothes the nerve and eliminates the pain transmissions to the brain for a period of time. The time will differ from person to person. Usually the pain can be controlled with one application on a cotton swab for up to two to three hours.

Put a few grains of cayenne pepper on the aching tooth and gum. This will hurt more at first, but it will go away soon, and so will your toothache.

If you have an aloe vera plant, cut a piece of a leaf and squeeze the gel directly on the aching tooth. Repeat as needed until the pain is gone.

A Sweet Side Effect

Here is a remedy that made us feel better in two different ways: vanilla extract. She would put some vanilla extract on a cotton ball and rub it on the sore area. The alcohol content of the vanilla will help to numb the toothache. And taking the vanilla out of the cupboard always made Grandma feel like baking.

Two Ways To Use Tea

Soak a white washcloth in a cup of prepared chamomile tea. Wring out the tea, and place the warm washcloth on the outside of your mouth (your cheek or jaw) in the area where your toothache is. Dip the washcloth in the tea again whenever it begins to cool. The chamomile should draw out the pain after a few applications.

Drinking sage tea can help relieve toothache pain. Make a stronger cup of tea than you usually would, and hold the tea in your mouth for about thirty seconds before you swallow. The pain should dissipate by the time you've drained your cup of tea.

Not For Teetotalers

One toothache remedy that should be reserved for adults only is whiskey. Soak a cotton ball in the beverage, and rub it on your troubling tooth and gum. The anesthetic qualities of the whiskey should hold you over until you can get to your dentist. Again, although the remedy doesn't call for you to drink the whiskey, it is still not recommended for children.

Grandpa's Yarrow Escape

Whenever Grandpa would get a toothache, Grandma would make him a yarrow poultice. She would steep a heaping teaspoon of yarrow in just a few ounces of boiling water. She would let it sit for a minute while she cut the cheesecloth. Then, she would strain the liquid and put the saturated herb in the cheesecloth. She'd give it to my Grandfather who would hold it on his aching tooth until he fell asleep in his favorite chair.

CHAPTER 4

THE BUZZ FACTOR: BEE STINGS

In the United States, the majority of problem bee stings come from honey bees and yellow jackets. If you are allergic and get stung, seek medical care immediately. The stinger should be carefully removed with tweezers as soon as possible.

It can be tricky to get a stinger out without releasing the poison into the body. Grandma was the expert bee-stinger remover around her house. She would pass a wet bar of soap over the area, and it seemed to come right out.

Take The Sting Out Of The Sting

Apply ammonia on a cotton ball to a bee sting for quick relief.

Since ancient times, mud or clay packs have been used to alleviate the discomfort of stings of all kinds. The cooling sensation and the mild drawing action help relieve the pain.

Ice packs or a few ice cubes placed in a piece of cheesecloth will dull the pain of a sting.

Tears And Celery

More than once when I was young, I ran into an angry hornet. If you've ever met a hornet, you know that their stings are one of the worst. They tend to cause more pain and discomfort than any other type of insect sting. Grandma would dry my tears, then she would have me chew a small piece of celery stalk and place the pasty mixture of saliva and celery on the site of the sting. Try this in an emergency. You will be pleasantly surprised that the throbbing and the pain will subside in a short period of time. Two or three applications will probably be needed to bring the bite under control.

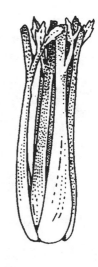

Swell Ideas For Reducing Swelling

Crush a charcoal tablet and place on a cotton ball. Attach to the sting with a Band-Aid to reduce pain and swelling.

A slice of cold onion placed on a bee sting or insect bite will stop pain and swelling.

Grandpa always had a chaw of tobacco with him, even though he tried to hide it from Grandma. It proved handy when any of us kids got stung by a bee. Moistened tobacco applied to a bee sting can help reduce pain and swelling.

Aspirin is one of the most common home remedies for a variety of complaints, even bee stings. Make into a paste with water and apply to reduce pain and swelling. Don't try this remedy if you're allergic to aspirin.

A paste made from baking soda can be used effectively once the stinger has been removed. A paste made from meat tenderizer, pineapple, or papaya will also work.

YOU SHOULD SEE THE OTHER GUY: CUTS AND SCRAPES

Cleaned And Dressed

One of the best treatments to cause fast blood coagulation is to place an "herbal bandage" on the cut using the herb yarrow. Both the leaves and the flower tips can be pressed into the wound before it is washed and bandaged.

Whenever you need to stop the bleeding from a small cut, rinse the area thoroughly and dress the wound with any of these substances: papaya pulp, cayenne pepper, a moist tea bag, goldenseal powder, or aloe vera gel.

An Oily Solution To Scarring

Applying vitamin E oil to a cut will help it heal more quickly and prevent scarring. Placing the membrane from inside an eggshell will also keep a scar from forming.

Sweet Ways To Guard Against Infection

One of the best natural remedies to prevent infection of a cut or serious bruise is to use juniper berries. Crush fresh berries to make a paste, apply to the wound in a poultice, and allow to remain for three to four hours.

The next time you get a cut, apply a liberal amount of honey to it to stop the bleeding quickly and prevent infection.

WHEN IT'S MUGGY AND BUGGY: OTHER INSECT BITES

Most insect bites are harmless, however some cause some discomfort and may be more serious, requiring professional medical attention. These include tick bites that can transmit Lyme disease or Rocky Mountain spotted fever, and mosquitoes that may carry malaria.

Just Say No

Avoid alcoholic beverages if you will be in an area with mosquitoes. Alcohol causes the blood to come closer to the surface, making you a tempting target.

Say Ahhh

Rub brewer's yeast and garlic into the affected area to help relieve discomfort. A slice of raw potato may also help.

Meat tenderizer can be used to relieve pain and itching. Dissolve a quarter to a half teaspoon in a small amount of warm water and apply to the bite.

Be Quick With A Tick

Ticks should be removed as soon as possible using a lighted match and tweezers. Hold the flame near the tick until it withdraws, then use the tweezers to remove it.

TIME FOR THE TWEEZERS: SPLINTERS

Place an ice cube on the splinter for a few seconds before trying to remove it. This will numb the area.

CHAPTER 5

OH, MY ACHING...

FEELING CREAKY: ARTHRITIS

In basic terms, arthritis is the inflammation of a joint. There are many types of arthritis, which may occur in any of the joints in the body. Most cases of arthritis are characterized by pain, swelling, and deterioration of the joint.

A tried and true remedy that works, depending on the severity of the arthritic condition, is to rub Ben-Gay on the affected area. This provides heat and soothes the discomfort.

Feeling Under The Weather

While grandmother really didn't know the cause of her joint aches and pains, she somehow knew that changes in the weather and certain foods seemed to irritate the problem. When she felt a flair up, she avoided tomatoes, potatoes that had any green on them, eggplant, red and green bell peppers (yellow was OK), all varieties of chili peppers, and paprika. What Grandma didn't know is that many of these vegetables fall into a category known as the nightshade family and may contain the chemical solanine. Solanine has been known to cause inflammation in animal studies.

Some Dos And Don'ts

Take one tablespoon of salmon oil daily at lunch and supper. Avoid milk since Vitamin D may irritate sore joints. Also, avoid red meats and paprika. Drink only distilled water.

Work It Out

Exercise is good for everybody. One of the prime benefits is increasing flexibility and keeping the joints in good working order. Nothing could be more important for the arthritis-sufferer. Also, strengthening the muscles will take stress off the joints. The exercise need not be strenuous. Walking and swimming are great options. Grandma started her day with a walk through the woods. "It gets you going!" she always said.

Try Some Alphabet Soup

It's amazing what good nutrition can do for you. Taking supplements of vitamins C, B6, and E can help relieve arthritis pain. The minerals calcium, zinc, magnesium, and beta-carotene may also be helpful. Whenever you add supplements to your daily routine, you should consult your doctor for the safe, effective dosage.

Some Hot Tips

Applying heat to aching joints makes good common sense. It certainly did to Grandma. She recommended a hot bath, heating pad, hot water bottle, or simply wrapping up in a snugly quilt.

Heat some coarse salt in a frying pan and make it into a poultice. Applying it to the affected parts of the body should draw out toxins and speed relief.

If you have arthritis, getting out of bed in the morning can be very difficult. Even if you don't have arthritis, you may feel stiff when you first wake up. Keeping your muscles warm during the night can prevent morning stiffness. Some people pile up the covers, use an electric blanket, a hot water bottle, or heating pad to keep warm. However, getting your night's rest in a sleeping bag seems to work the best, since it keeps in your body's own heat and distributes it more evenly. Just because you're using a sleeping bag doesn't mean you have to sack out on the floor, that would only make your stiffness worse. Stay in your own bed to get the benefit of this cure.

Take These Remedies With A Grain Of Salt

Folk wisdom says that carrying a raw potato in your pocket will draw the toxins out of the body and heal arthritic joints. Change the potato every couple of days as it darkens and dries up. If you prefer a more direct potato cure, cut up two cups unpeeled potatoes and boil them slowly in five quarts water until the liquid is reduced by half. Once the water is cool enough not to burn the skin, immerse a washcloth in the potato water and place it on the sore joints. Keep repeating this process until the pain lessens.

Grandma advised friends with arthritis to wear a copper bracelet. It's not specially scientific, but my grandmother swore by it. The worst part is that your wrist may turn green, but there won't be any other side-effects.

Folk wisdom tells us that rubbing joints once a week with peanut oil will prevent arthritis.

According to traditional German folk wisdom, a cat will carry away your arthritis pain. Have your pet tabby sit on the affected joint to cure your arthritis. Even if it doesn't work, you'll have spent some quality time snuggling with your cat.

Fish And Vinegar

Fish oil has given some people relief from arthritis symptoms. You can take it in capsule form, one a day for the average person. If you don't like to take supplements, try eating more fish. Be sure to choose varieties that are high in fat, such as salmon, tuna, and mackerel, among others.

When your symptoms flare up, try apple cider vinegar. You can either drink it or put it in your bath. If taking internally, add the vinegar and twice as much honey to a glass of warm water. Soak in hot water with one cup vinegar and one cup Epsom salts.

Fruit Juice For Your Joints

Eating cherries is a delicious way to fight arthritis pain. You can choose any variety you like. You can buy fresh, frozen, or canned. Drink at least one glass of cherry juice a day, the all-natural variety without sugar added that you can buy at your local health food store. Some traditional wisdom says you should drink plenty of cherry juice for four days in a row and then go four days without drinking any. Keep repeating this cycle to cure your arthritis. Other people benefit from eating regular amounts of cherries and drinking a glass of cherry juice every day. Experiment to see what works best for you.

White grape juice is reputed to absorb the bodily toxins that cause arthritis. Drink a glass at breakfast and another before dinner every day.

Try a tropical treat to reduce arthritis inflammation and pain. Drink a glass of fresh pineapple juice, twice a day, one after lunch and the other after dinner. If you don't have a juicer and can't find fresh pineapple juice at your local grocery or health food store, you can also used canned or bottled juice, as long as it is all-natural, without additives or preservatives.

Fresh Advice From Grandma's Garden

My grandmother planted an extensive garden every year, with vegetables, herbs, and flowers. There was nothing better than having a summer dinner at Grandma's house with plenty of homegrown food. I remember how fresh those string beans tasted. I could eat them every day. If you have arthritis, you should make it a point to eat string beans as often as possible. The combination of vitamins, minerals, and other compounds in this vegetable seem to correct the arthritic condition.

Grandma also had a flower garden that was the envy of her friends. Lucky for them, she liked to share—especially when it came to helping treat arthritis pain. Try this one yourself. As they begin to wilt, take the petals of three or four of the flowers and put them in a hot bath. You'll feel well-pampered, and your joints will thank you.

Rubbing You The Right Way

Rubbing painful joints with a soothing liniment or salve can bring down swelling and soothe discomfort. Try any one of these arthritis rubs: a mixture of a half tea-spoon eucalyptus oil and two tablespoons olive oil; ginger juice, made from squeezing grated fresh ginger root through a cheesecloth, combined with the same amount of sesame oil; and aloe vera gel, which can also be taken internally to treat arthritis. Gently massage the sore areas with any of these salves.

Rub the affected area with oil of bay. Grandmother used to take a few of the leaves and heat them in a small amount of pure olive oil using low heat for approximately thirty minutes. The oil never cooks if the heat is kept low. If the oil starts smoking, add a small amount of Canola oil. After allowing them to simmer for the thirty minutes strain off the oil and use the oil on the affected areas.

Grandma's Cornsilk Curative

To treat arthritis, my grandmother would walk out to her garden, pick a few ears of corn, and bring them back to her kitchen. She would shuck the corn and pick out the silk, putting about a hand-ful into a cup of hot water about ten minutes. When the tea had fin-ished steeping, she'd give a warm cupful of the brew to the arthri-tis sufferer. If you're not lucky enough to have a garden like Grandma, you can also use corn silk extract or dried corn silk which you can find at your local health food store.

Herbal Relief

A number of herbs are effective in reducing the pain of arthritis. Experiment with rosemary, nettles, basil and sage. You should take several cups of these herbal brews a day, either alone or in combination with one another.

The herb alfalfa relives some symptoms of arthritis. Take at least three to four cap-sules per day. You may also take alfalfa in the form of a tea three to four times a day to treat pain.

Brew a tea of fresh parsley by steeping one cup of the leaves in one quart boiling water for fifteen minutes. Strain and refrigerate. Take a half cup before your morn-ing meal and another before the evening meal. Take a dose whenever your arthri-tis pain becomes severe.

Remedies From Around The World

In traditional Romanian healing, celery is cooked in milk and eaten to treat arthri-tis. Celery does appear to have certain properties that lessen the symptoms of arthritis. You can also eat raw celery or juice the vegetable and drink it. Try to get some celery every day to lessen the effects of arthritis.

Seaweed is a regular part of the Japanese diet, and the incidence of arthritis in Japan is significantly lower than it is in the United States. If the idea of eating a lot of sushi doesn't appeal to you, take powdered kelp diluted with water instead. You can find kelp at most health food stores. Take a half teaspoon of the powder in a cup of warm water every evening before going to bed. You can also take kelp pills if you prefer.

Healing Miss Betsy

Arthritis doesn't seem to run in our family, and Grandma was spry and energetic her whole life. But her best friend and next door neighbor, Miss Betsy, suffered something terribly from rheumatism. Grandma would go next door whenever Miss Betsy's joints were really bothering her to whip up her cabbage cure. She'd take one of the cabbages from her garden and steam a few leaves in Miss Betsy's kitchen. My grandmother would then rub some olive oil into Miss Betsy's knees and ankles where she had her arthritis and when the cabbage leaves were just cool enough she'd lay them on top. Miss Betsy would cover her legs with a towel to keep the heat in, and they'd repeat the process about an hour later. Miss Betsy always said that if it weren't for Grandma and her cabbages she would have ended up bed-ridden, instead of being able to get up, play with her grandchildren and take care of her house.

A Little Smelly But Worth A Try

When you have an attack of arthritis pain, rub a fresh clove of garlic over the sore area. Taking two garlic pills or capsules each day can also help prevent symptoms.

Make a poultice by stirring three tablespoons of horseradish into a half cup boiled milk. Place the mixture in a piece of cloth and apply it to the affected joint. Leave the poultice on the sore area until it cools. You should feel much better.

No Pain, No Gain

Cayenne pepper cures many ailments, and it seems to have long-term benefits in treating arthritis pain. Take one or two cayenne capsules, three or four times a day, every day. The bad news is that you will probably notice an increase in pain at first. The good news is that quickly afterwards the pain will begin to decrease, and in the long run, you'll feel much relief from painful joints. Because this remedy does contribute to pain at first, you should only undertake this treatment with the help of your doctor.

LIFT FROM THE KNEES: BACK PAIN

Relaxation Therapy

The herb valerian root taken in capsule form or prepared as a tea tend to relive the discomfort through the relaxation of the muscles. Grandma's favorite for backache was to brew a pot of valerian root and add two tablespoons of honey. Drink one cup every two to three hours to achieve the desired relief.

Whenever anyone in her family had a bad back, Grandma recommended a soak in a hot tub with Epsom salts, not too long, about twenty minutes. Chiropractors and physical therapists often prescribe the same thing. Alternating hot and cold may also help, taking a hot bath or shower one day and applying an icepack to the sore area intermittently throughout the day the next.

A warm poultice can help relax muscles and speed relief from back pain. Try using flaxseeds the next time your back is tired and sore. Soak a cup of the seeds overnight. When you're ready to make your poultice, boil the seeds and tie them up in a piece of cloth when they have cooled just enough not to burn the skin.

The Straight And Yarrow

Taking a daily dosage of yarrow tea can help heal a problem back. Brew the tea from a teaspoon of dried yarrow and a cup of boiling water. After it steeps for ten minutes, strain and drink. Take a cup before each meal and one just before going to bed.

Leave On The Leaves

My grandmother's cabbage cure for arthritis is also helpful for treating back pain. Steam a few leaves until they're slightly wilted, about ten minutes. Rub the sore area with olive oil and place the cabbage leaves on top of it as soon as they are cool enough for you to stand. Be careful not to burn your skin. Put a towel over the area to retain the warmth. Leave it on for an hour and then repeat the whole process.

Healing Hands

A massage can bring relief from back pain for at least several hours, especially if you use Grandma's homemade rubbing liniment. Mix a pint of rubbing alcohol with three ounces wintergreen oil and two tablespoons powdered white willow bark. Allow to sit in the sun for two hours and strain. Warm slightly and massage the affected area.

Make a liniment from one pint rubbing alcohol, two ounces of wintergreen and a dozen aspirin. Massage into sore muscles. Don't try this remedy if you're allergic to aspirin.

Ideas From The East

Traditional Asian medicine recommends soaking your feet to ease a bad back. Leave your feet in warm water for twenty to thirty minutes.

Asian healers prescribe black beans to heal back pain. Get a bag of dried black beans at the grocery store and prepare them according to the instructions on the package, but without salt. Eat a couple of tablespoons of the beans every day for a month. Don't store the beans in the refrigerator for longer than three or four days. Make fresh batches as needed.

A Spoonful Of Relief

To promote overall healing, take cod liver oil, which is rich in Vitamins A and D. One tablespoon, three times a day will help aide in the healing process.

White willow bark contains the active ingredient salacin, an aspirin-like compound, effective for treating pain, including that of the back. It is usually taken in tincture form, one teaspoon three times per day for severe back pain.

TENNIS ANYONE?: BURSITIS

Bursitis is an inflammation of the bursae, small sacs filled with fluid found in the joints, bones, muscles and tendons. They cushion the bones against friction during movement. Numerous injuries of the bursae can occur, the most frequent from calcium deposits and increased stress on a particular area, such as the elbow with resulting "tennis elbow."

Grandma's Bursitis Plant

My grandmother came from Europe in the early 1900s. She didn't have much, just two bags and a plant she carried under her arm. When she came to Ellis Island, she was not allowed to bring her plant into the country. That well-travelled plant was the herb arnica. My grandfather had a serious problem with recurrent pain in both shoulders from doing heavy farm work for many years. The only thing that ever relieved his pain was a salve made from arnica. Although her plant didn't survive the journey, her remedy did: Prepare a salve by placing two tablespoons of powdered arnica in just enough olive oil to make a loose paste. This needs to be applied to the affected area twice per day and left on for twenty minutes. Cover it with a washcloth slightly dampened with water as hot as you can comfortably stand.

The Jekyll And Hyde Of Exercise

Exercising the affected joint is the most effective way to relieve discomfort. Ice packs will help reduce any swelling, which will speed the healing process.

Bursitis can be caused by overdoing exercise, pushing the body past its current fitness level. Exercise can also be the cure. The trick is to re-establish a full range of motion for sore muscles. You might try lifting weights, preferably under the supervision of a trainer or physical therapist. More simply, swing your arms in large circles in both direction, or stretch arms above your head by walking fingers up a wall. Remember that pain is a message. If a particular movement hurts, don't push it.

A Sleeping Cure For Shoulder Pain

Whenever someone in the family had bursitis or some other shoulder problem, Grandma would want to know how they had been sleeping, whether they laid on the arm with it above their head. Nine times out of ten, they did. She'd tell them to be careful of how they sleep, keeping the arm out of the way, and they'd usually feel better in a matter of days.

A SWELL JOINT: GOUT

Gout is related to uric acid levels in the blood, urine and tissues. The acid tends to crystallize in certain joints, especially the large toe. Ninety percent of the cases occur in men. Uric acid is derived from certain foods, and a low-purine diet is recommended. Foods high in purines are meat, anchovies, asparagus, herring and sardines.

Drier Is Better

If you have gout, avoid alcohol, even small amounts. Alcohol interferes with proper liver functioning, allowing more of the toxin that causes gout to build up in the body. Drinking alcohol also causes dehydration which can aggravate gout.

Teetotalers' Treatments

Hyssop tea gives relief from gout, especially if combined with juniper.

Certain herbal teas help clean out the toxins that cause gout. Yarrow, dandelion, and celery seed work especially well. You can use them individually or in combination with one another. Take three or four cups a day to keep gout away.

An old country cure for gout is a daily dose of corncob tea. Cut the kernels off several ears of fresh corn, put the cobs in a stew pot and cover liberally with water. Let the mixture simmer for an hour, remove the cobs, and retain the liquid. Store the corncob tea in a sealed jar in the refrigerator. After each meal, take a cup of the tea. Do this every day until the pain is gone.

Juicy Tidbits

An age-old cure for gout is to drink eight ounces of black cherry juice every day. This remedy may also affect some arthritic conditions.

To relieve the painful symptoms of gout, follow a mostly-strawberry diet. For several days, try to eat little besides strawberries. Certain substances in strawberries seem to relieve inflammation, which will reduce the discomfort caused by this ailment.

Garlic Lovers' Take Note

The traditional Russian remedy for gout is getting more fresh garlic into the system. Try to eat at least two cloves a day. You can mince the garlic and eat it in a salad or sprinkled over a meal. You can also swallow it with a glass of water, like a pill. This garlicky cure will keep away the gout, as well as vampires.

BE STILL MY ACHING HEAD: HEADACHES

Most headaches are caused by stress, diseases related to the eyes and sinuses, high fevers, or allergies to perfumes, after shave lotions and other products. Poor alignment of the cervical vertebrae may also contribute.

A number of herbs made into teas cab be used effectively to reduce a headache's severity or totally relieve it. These include goldenseal, hyssop, lobelia, mint and burdock root.

Grandma's 30-Minute Migraine Mend

One day my Aunt Beatrice was suffering from a severe headache, the kind that would probably be called a migraine today. To relieve her pain, grandma peeled several bananas. Although Aunt Beatrice said she wasn't hungry, Grandma kept right on peeling. To our surprise, she put aside the fruit and made a poultice of the skins. She placed the poultice on my Aunt's forehead and back of her neck. The headache was gone in about thirty minutes. And we all enjoyed the banana bread after supper.

Brushing Away Headache Pain

Whenever somebody in the family got a headache, Grandma would take out her favorite silver-handled hairbrush and gently brush their hair, away from the temples and down the back of the head. She would hum a little tune, just under her breath, and it wasn't too long before the headache was gone and you felt much better. It appears that brushing helps increase blood flow to the area which speeds relief.

Forehead—Aches

For this old world cure, all you need is a potato and a bandanna or towel. Slice the potato and stick it under the bandanna tied tightly around your forehead. The combination of moisture and pressure eases the pain.

Whenever my grandmother got a headache, she would dip a rag in vinegar and tie it around her forehead until the pain disappeared. She'd usually be feeling better in an hour or two.

Rub your forehead and temples with a lemon peel, with the rind against your skin. Secure it in place with a bandanna and leave it there until the headache is gone.

Cold Cures

Apply an ice pack to the back of the neck or forehead for headache relief.

Try the cold water cure for a headache. Fill your bath tub with cold water, just enough to cover your feet, and walk back and forth for a few minutes, no more than five. The rest of your body should be covered and warm. Once your feet begin to feel warm in the cold water, get out, dry off your feet, and get into bed. Snuggle down into your covers, rest, and your headache should disappear pretty quickly.

Advice From Our Forefathers

Colonial Americans treated headaches with a mixture of one teaspoon honey and a half teaspoon garlic juice.

Another sage idea: grate some fresh horseradish and make a poultice out of it. Apply it to the back of your neck to relieve headache pain.

Pressing Possibilities

By rubbing the roof of your mouth with your thumb you can interfere with the nerves' ability to carry pain signals. Press into a certain spot for five minutes and then move to another place on the roof of your mouth. You should feel relief almost immediately.

Traditional Chinese healers prescribe acupressure to relieve headache pain. Take turns rubbing the second joint of each thumb, first the right and then the left, for two minutes each. Repeat five times on each thumb. If you use your favorite scented lotion, you can imagine you're getting a hand massage at the manicurist.

Aspirin Alternatives

Aspirin will cure a headache, but it upsets some people's stomachs. Almonds contain the same active ingredient, so try eating a couple dozen almonds in place of taking aspirin. It might not work as quickly, but it tastes much, much better!

Strawberries contain a compound that is similar to the active ingredient in aspirin. If you'd rather not take over-the-counter medication to get rid of your headache, try eating a few strawberries instead.

Vaporize A Headache

Grandma kept a big jar of Vick's vapor rub on her bedside table. When she had a headache at night, she'd put a dab on each temple to open up her sinuses and relieve pressure and pain. You don't have to wait for bedtime. Use this remedy any time a headache has you down. Also, if you prefer, you can use peppermint oil instead of Vick's. If it's not comfortable to apply the oil directly to the skin, take a hot bath, using a few drops in the water, and breathe deeply. Oil of rosemary also helps get rid of a headache. Put a few drops on your temples and under your nose.

Breathing in vinegar vapors can help relieve a headache. Mix a cup of apple cider vinegar and a cup of water and bring to a boil. When the mixture begins to steam, turn the heat down as far as it will go, place a towel over your head, and breathe in the vapors, for about ten minutes.

TAMING HORSES: LEG CRAMPS

Leg cramps may be caused by a number of circulatory problems. Inefficient blood flow in the lower extremities is common as you age. One of the most frequent complaints is called intermittent claudication.

Get The Kinks Out Of Your Diet

There are a number of vitamins that may help relieve leg cramps. Vitamin B-6 has had good results, but check with your doctor for dosage recommendations before you try these.

Vitamin E benefits the circulatory system in many ways, and it seems to have positive effects in relieving night foot and leg cramps. Take up to 400 IU of vitamin E daily. For higher doses, you should consult a physician.

People who take diuretics may suffer from leg cramps. If this is the case, add bananas to your diet to make sure you get enough potassium. A banana or two each day should replace the potassium you are losing.

Since this is sometimes caused by a deficiency of calcium and magnesium it would be wise to consume foods that are high in these minerals such as dark green leafy vegetables and whole grains.

You may be able to reduce the occurrences of leg cramps by changing your eating habits. Leg cramps my be an indication of a

calcium deficiency, so be sure to include plenty of greens in your diet. Eat them raw or steamed to get the most benefits from the vegetable's nutrients. Also, try eating less sugar, white flour and fatty meats for a week. See if you notice a difference.

Stretch It Out

If you feel a muscle about to tighten up, take a moment and stretch it. You can also stretch a muscle that's already cramping, but the technique is more effective if you use it to ward off a cramp.

Improving your blood circulation can prevent muscle cramps. When you wake up in the morning, and when you go to bed at night, lie on your back and raise your legs above your body. Lean your legs against a wall, the end of the bed, etc., and keep them elevated for about ten minutes. Twice a day should do the trick.

Putting Discomfort To Bed

Grandma was always after us kids to keep our feet warm. She was convinced that walking around on a cold floor could bring on leg cramps. If you have a problem with spasms in the legs and feet, try wearing a pair of warm, wool socks to bed.

Leg cramps that occur at night can be relieved with this sweet and sour remedy. In half a glass of warm water, mix one teaspoon of honey with one teaspoon of apple cider vinegar and one tablespoon of calcium lactate. You should be feeling better in less than half an hour.

Wash Away The Pain

Here's a soothing tea that can wash away leg cramps. Some say if you drink one cup of red raspberry leaf tea twice a day—in the morning and in the evening—you may say good-bye to leg cramps for good.

Pinch Away The Pain

Try this remedy in a pinch. Some say it works almost instantly. When you first feel a leg cramp, pinch the skin between your upper lip and your nose with your thumb and index finger. Put your fingers on either side of the "divet" and keep pinching this point for about twenty seconds and the cramps should disappear. This is especially effective for people who get leg cramps while swimming.

BLINDED BY THE LIGHT: MIGRAINE

This severe throbbing headache, normally centered behind an eye or at the back of the head, may last for ten to fifteen hours before subsiding.

The herbs feverfew and ginko have had excellent success in treating migraines. Feverfew reduces or eliminates the pain, while gingko biloba increases circulation.

Grandma's Cabbage Compress

The next time you get a migraine, try my Grandmother's cabbage leaf compress. Our Aunt Beatrice was a migraine sufferer, and she would always turn to one of Grandma's remedies for relief. I remember this remedy was called upon quite a bit. Soften a few leaves in boiling water—just dip the leaves in until they get soft.

When they cool off a bit, place a leaf or two on your forehead and a leaf or two on the nape of your neck. Grandma would keep the cabbage in place by wrapping bandannas around Beatrice's head and neck. Once the leaves are secure, relax and let the cabbage do its work. Grandma claimed that the cabbage would draw out the pain, so when she threw the leaves away, she said she was throwing the pain away.

Pressure Is The Point

Acupressure can be helpful for many ailments. Try this technique the next time you feel a migraine coming on. With your right thumb, apply pressure to your left palm. Keep the pressure firm—especially if you're feeling tenderness in the area—for five minutes, then switch hands and repeat.

Look Good, Feel Better

Some people find that sitting under a hair dryer relieves migraine tension. The heat and hum of the dryer can be very relaxing and very effective.

Hold The Cold Cuts

If you are prone to migraines, keep a jar of very strong mustard on hand. When you feel the pain coming on, open the jar and breath the fumes deeply. Many people have found this helps relieve their discomfort.

Try the double Spanish onion remedy. Boil two onions, one is for eating and one is for mashing into a poultice and placing on your forehead.

LOOSEN UP: MUSCLE STIFFNESS

This is a common complaint. Certainly anybody who has done intensive manual labor or has worked out too vigorously at the gym has had stiff muscles or a backache. One of the best herbs to relieve muscle stiffness is chamomile. To prepare a massage oil, place three cups fresh chamomile flowers in a pint bottle and add enough extra virgin olive oil to cover them. Place the mixture in direct sunlight for two to three weeks, then refrigerate until you need to use it. The oil may be warmed to a comfortable temperature.

Soothing Soaks

My grandmother kept Epsom salts in the cupboard where she stored the ingredients for her home remedies. It was one of the products to which she turned most. Nothing is more relaxing than settling into a hot bath with Epsom salts. The salts, which are mostly magnesium, greatly ease tension and also draw out the fluids which often collect in tired muscles.

Here are two bathtub suggestions that are effective for helping a charley horse. Make a relaxing ginger bath by preparing a strong ginger tea. Boil two teaspoons of ginger powder or fresh ginger root in two cups of boiling water. When the water turns yellowish in color, the ginger tea is ready to be added to your bath. Soak for a relaxing twenty to thirty minutes to relieve muscle stiffness. Ginger is also excellent for the circulation.

The other charley horse bath is one you've probably heard of. That's because it usually does the trick. Pour three cups of Epsom salt in a warm bath. Soak for twenty to thirty minutes to ease the pain.

Make Lemonade

For muscle stiffness (especially for a charley horse) try this citrus solution. In a blender, place two small oranges cut into pieces, three small lemons cut up and one small grapefruit cut into pieces. Be sure to use the whole fruit, skin and all. Add one teaspoon of cream of tartar and blend. Place the citrus blend in a covered jar or bottle and store in the refrigerator. Twice a day—when you wake up and right before you go to bed—take two tablespoons of the citrus blend with two tablespoons of water.

Homemade Muscle Rubs

For an old Hungarian remedy for sore muscles, mix cayenne pepper with vegetable oil and rub into the affected area. Use a quarter to a half teaspoon pepper to one cup warm vegetable or baby oil. Cayenne pepper contains the active ingredient capsaicin that blocks the transmission of pain signals.

Make ginger juice by grating the ginger and squeezing it through cheesecloth. Measure the juice and add an equal part sesame oil. Massage the mixture onto your sore muscles as needed.

Hot And Cold Running Cures

Both heat and cold have their places in treating sore muscles. If you strain a muscle while working or exercising, apply an ice pack as soon as possible, no more than twenty minutes after the injury. This will help reduce swelling and pain. Taking a hot shower helps relax muscles which relieves pain. Direct the shower stream to the sore area. If you place a washcloth on the spot, it will retain heat and increase the relaxing effect.

The Farmers' Muscle Salve

My grandmother was always on the lookout for new remedies. One day while she was at the drugstore, she saw several elderly farmers ask Mr. Simpson, the pharmacist for the same thing, one right after the other. They all wanted wintergreen rubbing alcohol and a bottle of aspirin. Mr. Simpson explained to Grandma that they dissolved the aspirin in the alcohol to treat sore muscles and joints. A number of his customers swore by it. Grandma added the two items to her list, and it's been one of her favorite remedies for muscle ache ever since. Of course, she never gave it to anyone who was allergic to aspirin.

Apple cider vinegar is another sore muscle solution. Slowly boil two cups of apple cider vinegar and one tablespoon of cayenne pepper in a glass saucepan. Put it in a jar or bottle and use it on your sore muscles.

CHAPTER 6

HOW TO BE A REGULAR JOE OR JANE: CONSTIPATION

This occurs when waste material moves too slowly through the large intestines. It is caused by a low fiber diet, lack of moisture, or both. A number of drugs may also cause constipation, especially those with a high iron content.

The Java Jolt

For many people a cup of regular coffee seems to relieve constipation. Caffeine activates the peristaltic action of the intestines.

Diet Additions

Herbs commonly used to treat constipation include hyssop, flax seed and psyllium seed. Prunes act as a natural laxative. Over-the-counter preparations can be over-used and may reduce good bacteria in the intestinal tract.

Eat a high fiber diet, with at least three to four servings of fruits and vegetables and two to three servings of whole grains a day. This diet, along with adequate liquids, will alleviate the problem in a day or two.

Eat a baked apple for supper and another for breakfast the next morning. This works almost every time and is a lot more pleasant than an enema.

Believe it or not, a little Mexican food can help you get back on track. That's because eating an avocado mixture, very much like guacamole, can ease constipation. Mash up a ripe avocado and some chopped onion, a little lemon juice, and a dash of cumin. Enjoy your fiesta!

Persimmons may also help relieve constipation. Eat one a day when they're in season.

Soybeans Do The Trick

For a natural cure for constipation, boil two to three tablespoons of black soybeans in two quarts of water for ten to fifteen minutes. Simmer and reduce until there is only one quart left. The mixture can be seasoned as desired. Consume one glass three times a day until the problem is alleviated.

Friends and Enemas

When it came to constipation, Grandma said an enema bag was your best friend. She also swore by two tablespoons of mineral oil before bedtime. Lucky for us kids, she gave us a choice. So unless we were doubled over with discomfort, we would always take the mineral oil.

Grandma's Constitutional—A Constipation Cure

Grandma was always busy, working in her garden, canning vegetables, baking bread, visiting with company, but she made time every day for a long walk. Her morning constitutional, she called it. Exercise has many health benefits, including preventing and relieving constipation. You don't have to do wind sprints either. A mild stroll for fifteen minutes every day should help keep you regular.

Natural Laxatives

The natural, water-soluble fiber psyllium aids in moving food through the digestive tract. You can get psyllium seeds at your local health food store. Use them on other foods or simply take a teaspoon a day, chew, and swallow with a glass of water.

Flaxseeds have properties similar to psyllium. Make a laxative "goop," with flaxseeds ground in a coffee grinder mixed with apples, oranges, and grapefruit processed in a blender. Take three tablespoons of ground flaxseed with an equal amount of fruit everyday.

Escarole, spinach, okra, and Spanish onions are natural laxatives. Try eating escarole or spinach raw in salads. If you prefer, you can boil the escarole and drink the juice. Gumbo is a delicious way to get more okra in your diet. Eat roasted Spanish onions, preferably in the evening before going to bed. If you start the day by eating two small, fresh beets, you should have no problems with your digestive tract functioning.

Another of nature's most perfect foods is brewer's yeast. It is highly nutritious, a concentrated source of many vitamins and minerals. It also helps ease constipation. Many people take brewer's yeast in combination with wheat germ. The optimal dosage for most people seems to be a teaspoon of brewer's yeast and another of wheat germ. But start out slowly to give your body a chance to adjust to the change in your diet.

Salty, But Sweet Relief

Sauerkraut juice helps relieve constipation. If you don't want to make your own, like Grandma did, you can get it canned and drain the juice. You won't want to use this remedy too often, since it's very salty and excessive amounts of salt can be harmful.

Herbs That Make Scents—And A Little Pressure

There are several herbs that treat constipation. Sacred bark usually starts to work eight hours after it's taken. Senna is used in a number of over-the-counter laxatives. Goldenseal and bayberry are also helpful.

Certain scents seem to have positive effects on a constipation problem. Draw yourself a warm bath and add twelve or so drops of rosa gallica. Enjoy your bath for at least fifteen minutes and repeat three times a week.

Traditional Chinese medicine recommends acupressure to get rid of constipation. Rub the spot between your bottom lip and chin. Keep doing this until you begin to feel relief. It shouldn't take more than fifteen minutes.

Bulk Up On Fiber

Bulk up on fiber, which helps keep the digestive tract functioning regularly, by adding raw bran to your favorite cereal. You should give your body time to adjust to the higher level of fiber in your diet by starting out slowly, with a teaspoon or so, and working up to a tablespoon or two.

A Spoonful Of Relief

Olive oil is a wonderful food. It is a staple of fine cooking, and it tastes great. This delicious oil has many health benefits, as well. It helps lower cholesterol and helps the digestive tract function normally. You can take olive oil as a natural laxative, one tablespoon in the morning and another after dinner.

Grandma's huge jar of blackstrap molasses came in handy when someone in her family was constipated. An hour before lunch, she would have them take a teaspoon of the molasses in about a half cup of water. It seemed to clear the problem right up.

Rise And Shine

Start your morning with a fresh glass of juice. If you prefer fruit juice, drink orange or grapefruit. Any number of vegetable juices will help relieve constipation, including cucumber, celery, cabbage, and beet. Carrot juice seems to be especially helpful. Taking a tablespoon of aloe vera juice, available at the local health food store, twice a day, once in the morning and once before bed, is a fine remedy for constipation.

To help yourself have a bowel movement in the morning, drink a cup of warm water with the juice of half a lemon in it before having anything to eat. You can also drink prune juice, or eat prunes, apples, figs, or papaya for breakfast to stimulate the bowels.

Cure constipation with cloves. Before going to bed, fill a mug with half a cup of boiling water and add six or so cloves. Let it set overnight and drink the water in the morning. You'll be on your way to more regular bowel movements.

BULKING UP: DIARRHEA

Characterized by frequent, loose, watery stools, and abdominal cramping, diarrhea can be caused by drugs, bacterial infections, spoiled foods and a number of diseases. It is associated with dehydration and subsequent mineral loss. Medications should not be administered for at least 36 hours to give the body a chance to rid itself of the toxin that is causing the problem.

Combine one teaspoon finely chopped raw garlic with one teaspoon of honey. Take this remedy three times a day, about two hours after each meal.

Grandma's Juicy Secrets

Grandma learned from her mother to always keep blackberry juice in the ice box for these occasions. She had us drink four ounces of the juice and we'd be feeling "right and steady" in no time. Blackberries are a tasty and effective treatment for diarrhea. You can take the blackberries in many different forms: frozen, fresh, or even blackberry wine. Try this recipe to make a gallon of blackberry wine: Crush four quarts of wild blackberries, add a gallon of boiling water, and let stand 24 hours. Add three pounds sugar and strain. When it starts bubbling, it's time to bottle it.

Bananas add fiber and potassium to your system which helps relieve diarrhea. This is one remedy you won't have trouble getting your children to take!

Another of grandma's cures for diarrhea was to grate up one large apple and allow it to stand at room temperature for three to four hours until it turned brown before eating it. When the pectin oxidizes it tends to produce a chemical that is found in many over-the-counter remedies for diarrhea.

Dairy Does It

The good bacteria in yogurt and acidophilus capsules helps balance bad bacteria in the intestines and remedies diarrhea.

Combine two tablespoons cottage cheese and two teaspoons sour cream. Take the mixture three or more times a day, depending on the severity of the problem, until the diarrhea clears up.

Cure For Cramps

Use ginger tea to alleviate pain or cramping. Chamomile tea may be helpful in slowing the diarrhea or stopping it completely.

Ice packs can take away the discomfort associated with diarrhea. Put one on the middle of your back and another on your lower back. Leave the ice on for ten minutes and then take it off for ten minutes. Keep going this way as long as it feels good.

Bland, But Beneficial

You should follow a bland diet, with plenty of complex carbohydrates, while you have diarrhea. Try eating mostly rice, potatoes, bananas, toast, and apples.

It's always a good idea to add brown rice, something of a wonder food, to your diet. It's low in fat, high in complex carbohydrates and fiber, and an excellent source of B vitamins. Following a diet high in fiber can help keep the digestive tract functioning smoothly, preventing both diarrhea and constipation. If you do come down with a bout of diarrhea, you can also use the rice water to cure the problem. Boil a half cup brown rice in six cups of water for thirty minutes. Strain the rice and retain the water. Sweeten it with honey and drink one cup every other hour. Do not drink any other liquids until the diarrhea clears up.

From the ancient Greeks to Grandma, barley water has long been used to cure diarrhea. Put a quarter cup of barley in six cups of water, boiling until the liquid is reduced by half. Strain out the barley, and keep both it and the water. Drink the barley water as a tea, using lemon and honey to flavor it if you like. It will help keep you hydrated as it returns your bodily systems to normal. You should also eat the barley, which is good for you anyway.

Restoring Friendly Bacteria

Drink one to two glasses a day of any of these beverages: buttermilk, sauerkraut juice, or kefir, a product you can find in your local health food store. These substances help restore friendly bacteria to the system that prevent the bad bacteria that cause diarrhea. You can also get these helpful bacteria by eating pickled vegetables or raw sauerkraut.

Lousy Timing—A Tip For Travelers

There's nothing worse than getting sick while on vacation. Unfortunately, diarrhea often strikes when we drink water that contains bacteria our bodies aren't used to. This is a standard remedy relied upon by international travelers and recommended by various nations' health services. Pour a glass of orange juice, or any other fruit juice, and mix it with half a teaspoon of honey and a pinch of salt. Fill another glass with purified water. Drink from one glass and then the other. Keep alternating beverages until all the liquid has been consumed. You should feel better by the next morning.

CHAPTER 7

HERE'S THE SKINNY

ARE YOU GONNA EAT THAT?: APPETITE

B-complex vitamins stimulate the appetite center in the brain. To increase your appetite, take a half teaspoon of brewer's yeast, an excellent source of these vitamins, daily. If you are on a weight control program you should try and regulate your intake of Vitamin B and not overdo them with supplements.

ALL DAMMED UP: WATER RETENTION

One of the best diuretics to reduce excess water retention is watermelon or cucumber tea. Many melons work as a diuretic since they contain a chemical called cucurbocitrin. This chemical increases the ability of the cells to release fluids to the kidney's for release.

BATHROOM SCALE BLOWOUT: WEIGHT CONTROL

Grandma's Flapjack Diet

 Believe it or not, Grandma believed in eating buckwheat pancakes to lose weight. This is one great way to take off the pounds and enjoy yourself at the same time. Two pancakes for breakfast will keep you from getting hungry for at least five hours and will reduce your desire for heavy meals the balance of the day. It's a great appetite suppresser and much more fun to eat than celery and carrots.

Fill Up On Liquids

There are many herbal teas that you can buy at the health food store that are quite good for curbing the appetite: raspberry leaves, fennel seeds, yerba mate (this contains caffeine), cleavers and horehound. Use one tea bag, or if you prefer, one teaspoon of the dried herb. Drink one cup of tea a half hour before each meal and another cup before you go to bed.

To help you feel full, drink tomato juice ten or fifteen minutes before you eat.

Sweets Relief

To help curb your desire for sweets, slowly drink three ounces of pure grape juice diluted with one ounce of water a half hour before each meal and before you go to bed. Take several minutes to drink and be sure the grape juice has no sugar added and no additives or preservatives. Your cravings for desserts should start to disappear, making it easier for you to make healthy food choices.

CHAPTER 8

IN WITH THE GOOD AIR, OUT WITH THE BAD

SPRING IS IN THE AIR: HAY FEVER

Hay fever effects the mucous membranes of the nose and causes the eyes to tear. Many sufferers have symptoms all year long, especially a runny nose. Some people who have hay fever also suffer from asthma and occasional dermatitis (skin disorders).

Before The Sniffles Start

Hay fever is caused by pollen, so keep your house and car windows closed and the air conditioning on during hay fever season to help reduce pollen levels.

When you get inoculated against a disease, a small amount of inactive pathogen is introduced into your system to help your body build up its own natural defenses. You can do the same thing with hay fever by gradually building up your immunity to granules of bee pollen. Some people are allergic to bee pollen, some quite severely, so start very slowly. Begin with three small granules, and very, very slowly work your way up to a teaspoon a day. You can take the granules like pills with a glass of water or add them to your food. You can find bee pollen granules at your local health food store or from a beekeeper in your area. Begin the immunization process four months before hay fever season begins.

Supplemental Advice

Take 400IU Vitamin E capsules twice a day. One tablespoon of liquid alfalfa should also be taken twice a day.

Since colds and hay fever have many of the same symptoms, taking Vitamin C may help speed relief for hay fever sufferers. Take 500 to 1,000 milligrams a day until the symptoms clear up. However, you should check with your doctor for the exact dosage.

Plan ahead for hay fever season by taking brewer's yeast, according to the recommended dosage on the package. In addition to alleviating some of the worst allergy symptoms, it's also highly nutritious, a great source of various vitamins and minerals.

Cupboard Cures

Consuming two to three tablespoons of locally produced honey seems to eliminate the problem completely. The honey must be produced locally, not just any honey will do.

Take one to two tablespoons of apple cider vinegar a day during hay fever season.

Botannical Brews

As far back as the ancient Egyptians, the herb fenugreek has been used to treat all sorts of respiratory problems, including hay fever. Start drinking a cup of fenu-greek tea before every meal at the beginning of spring in March and keep it up for three months. Fenugreek is very powerful medicine and can provide a great deal of relief from congestion and other hay fever symptoms. To make the tea, take four cups cold filtered water and soak nine teaspoons fenugreek seed for six hours. Boil the mixture for three minutes, strain, and drink the tea sweetened with a small amount of honey.

Taking red clover blossoms or horseradish can help increase your resistance to a variety of allergies. Brew a tea from red clover blossoms and take up to four cups a day. You should be able to find red clover blossoms at your local health food store. Mix a quarter teaspoon of horseradish in a glass of juice or hide it in your food, taking a dose every day. Either one of these remedies should strengthen your system and keep you from suffering extreme allergy symptoms.

If you prefer not to take synthetic antihistamines, either over-the-counter preparations or drugs prescribed by a doctor, take nettle to get a natural antihistamine. Take a capsule or two every few hours to stave off sneezing, congestion, irritated eyes, and other hay fever symptoms.

Inhaling Healing

Make yourself a cup of your favorite herbal tea and inhale the vapors to lessen congestion due to hay fever.

Inhaling steam from warm salt water can help open nasal passages. You can also squirt warm salt water directly into your nostrils to clear out a stuffy nose. Dissolve a teaspoon of salt in one cup warm water. Dip with your hand and inhale with one nostril while pinching the other closed.

According to aromatherapists, the scent of lavender or chamomile can relieve hay fever symptoms. You can buy these essential oils at a local health food or herb store. Put a few drops on a hanky and keep it with you. Whenever you feel a sneezing fit coming on, press the handkerchief to your nose to bring the much needed relief.

Quick Relief

My grandmother used to tell anyone who had hay fever or sinus problems to lie down with a cool, wet washcloth over their face. It helps stop sneezing and eye irritation.

During hay fever season, keep honeycomb stocked in your home. Take a small piece and chew on it when you feel an attack coming on. Keep it in your mouth for ten to fifteen minutes, and of course, spit it out when you're finished. You don't need a ball of wax in your stomach. It should provide relief from hay fever symptoms.

SOMEBODY STOP ME: HICCUPS

A Spoonful Of Sugar

Whenever we would get the hiccups, Grandma would reach for the sugar bowl. Sugar cures hiccups by stimulating the nerve pathways that are transmitting the hiccup reflex signals. Just a spoonful of sugar should do the trick.

Culinary Curatives

To cure hiccups, try a cup of dill leaf tea sipped slowly.

Common wisdom suggests drinking various sorts of juice to cure hiccups, including orange, pineapple and onion.

Grandma considered apple cider vinegar the great cure-all. It was one of her favorite remedies for the hiccups. She would mix a teaspoon of the vinegar in a cup of warm water and have me drink it all down. By the time I finished the last drop, my hiccups would invariably be gone.

Chewing very slowly and thoughtfully can help interrupt the hiccup reflex. Pick something bready and chewy, like a bagel or slightly stale loaf bread. By the time you finish it, the hiccups should be gone.

Take A Deep Breath

Breathe into a paper bag to stop hiccups. Inhaling carbon dioxide appears to return the body back to normal. Concentrating on breathing may also help relax the diaphragm.

Aromatherapists recommend taking deep breaths of sandalwood oil or perfume to ease hiccups.

Pucker Up

Grandma recommended sucking on something sour, like a pickle, to get rid of the hiccups. The shock of a strong taste may jolt the diaphragm's nerves out of their spasms.

Suck on a wedge of lemon with a little Worcestershire sauce on it. This should get rid of your hiccups in a matter of no time.

RATTLE AND HUM: SNORING

Whether you're the snorer or the snoree, snoring can wreak havoc on a good night's sleep. Although in most cases the sleep partner gets the brunt of the abuse, snoring can indicate a potentially harmful

condition known as sleep apnea—a condition which literally deprives the brain of oxygen for a short time. In other words, the snorer stops breathing multiple times during the night. This deprives the person of the necessary deep level of sleep, so even though they are sleeping, the body isn't getting the rest it needs. If you have a chronic snoring problem (don't worry, your sleep partner will tell you), you may want to consult your physician.

Using a humidifier can end snoring caused by dry air.

Changing Positions

If you or your spouse only has an occasional snoring problem, you might have success if the snorer doesn't sleep on his or her back. Simply having the snorer turn on his side or stomach should let both of you sleep more soundly. You might try placing a pillow under the snorer's back so it is more difficult for him to roll over in his sleep.

Sometimes, a little levity can be the cure. Raising the head of your bed can help the snorer breath easier, thereby cutting back on the snoring. Try putting bricks or wood blocks under the legs of the bed. Simply placing an extra pillow under the snorer's head may only aggravate the problem.

CHAPTER 9

QUIT YOUR BELLY-ACHING!

LETTING THE AIR OUT: COLIC

Colic is probably caused by intestinal gas. Symptoms include crying, clenched fists, bulging abdominal area and whining.

There are many benefits to breast feeding your baby. Breast milk contains the nutrients a baby needs, boosts the child's immunity, and lets you snuggle and bond with your baby. However, if you eat dairy products, your breast milk may cause colic in your child. Experiment with your diet, eliminating dairy and getting the calcium you need from other sources, such as whole grains and green leafy vegetables. This remedy works in about half the cases of colic.

Grandma's Rock-A-Bye Baby Method

When babysitting for colicky infants, Grandma used to place one to two ounces of ginger ale into their bottles. She said this would soothe the discomfort almost all of the time. The carbonation helps the release of gas. Try and get the baby to burp on your shoulder. This will also solve the problem. Grandma's favorite remedy: Rock the baby in a rocking chair.

Baby's Belly Brews

Brew a tea of one teaspoon fennel seed and a quarter teaspoon sugar. Cool, strain, and pour into your child's bottle. It will calm the baby and help get rid of gas.

Add one ounce fresh peppermint leaves to a pint of boiling water and steep. The peppermint tea should be lukewarm when given to the child. A quarter cup will usually ease the symptoms and help the child sleep. You can also try letting your child suck on a peppermint stick. Not all children can tolerate peppermint's pungent taste. If your baby has trouble with it, try another remedy.

Make a tea from caraway seeds to soothe a colicky baby. Steep a tablespoon of caraway seeds in a cup of boiling water for ten minutes. Cool and strain out the seeds. A couple of teaspoons should be enough to ease gas pains and soothe the infant. You can give it to the baby in a bottle.

The Tried And True

Put corn syrup on your child's pacifier to help ease colic, or add a quarter teaspoon brown sugar to an eight ounce bottle of milk. It should help the baby expel gas. Of course, you don't want to overdo the sugar. That won't be good for the baby's teeth.

My grandmother found that simple cures were often quite effective. Warmth will help soothe a colicky baby. Try filling a hot water bottle with warm, not hot, water and place on the child's stomach. Or you can just hold your baby close and soothe the child with the warmth of your body and your loving touch.

FRIDGE FRIGHT: FOOD POISONING

Here's an antidote for food poisoning from bad shellfish. Bring two pints of water to a rapid boil, add two teaspoons cherry bark, one tablespoon fresh, grated ginger root and one finely diced onion. Allow the mixture to simmer ten minutes, remove from heat and allow to steep for thirty minutes. Drink two cups while it is still warm.

A RAGING INFERNO: HEARTBURN

This burning sensation in the abdomen is related to the excess release of hydrochloric acid, causing irritation to the stomach lining and the esophagus. Certain foods and liquids can cause this reaction, including coffee (more than two cups a day), alcohol, carbonated beverages, citrus fruits, tomato products and certain spices.

Tranquil Tummy Teas

A tea made from ginger soothes the stomach and controls the excess release of acid.

Slippery elm bark has been used for many years to ease an acid stomach and relieve heartburn discomfort. Look for this herb at your local health food store. You can use the bark itself or a pow-  der made from it, one teaspoon of either in a cup of boiling water. Sip the tea, and you should feel better shortly.

Undoing A Sugar Overdose

You know how kids are. They love sweet stuff, and sometimes they don't know when to quit. That's exactly the way I was as a child, especially at Grandma's house where there were so many delicious treats waiting for me in her kitchen. Whenever I ate too many of her goodies, Grandma would shake her head and say, "Poor thing. You've got a sore tummy, don't you?" Then she'd whip up her favorite remedy to settle a stomach sick from eating too many sugary sweets. She'd mix a cup of warm water, the juice of half a lemon, and a teaspoon of salt. She'd put her arm around me and tell me to drink it down slowly. It wasn't very long before I was feeling much better and looking for my next cookie.

Chew On This

Sometimes you can chew your way to heartburn relief. Take a mouthful of dry oats and chew until it's soft enough to swallow. Your favorite chewing gum can also reduce stomach acid and prevent heartburn.

Eating six unblanched almonds, chewing them very slowly and thoroughly, can help reduce acid in the stomach and soothe the discomfort.

You can also eat raw carrots to counteract heartburn. Peel them and chew each bite slowly and thoroughly.

Make-It-Better Beverages

Place one raw potato, that has been thoroughly washed with the skin still on, in a juicer. Dilute the juice evenly with water and drink three times a day. The potato juice must be made fresh.

Grandma preferred leaf lettuce to iceberg, but she always grew some iceberg lettuce to use in her heartburn remedy. Puree a few lettuce leaves and three quarters cup cold water in your blender. Sip the green liquid and prepare for relief.

One tablespoon raw apple cider vinegar mixed with cold water and sipped slowly during a meal is an effective treatment. Do not consume any other liquid with your meal.

This remedy sounds like it would do more to upset your stomach than settle it, but many people swear by it. Combine an egg white with two tablespoons of olive oil and drink all of the mixture.

Feel The Burn? Reach For Peppermint!

Grandpa loved to eat. Grandma was a wonderful cook, so they had a very happy marriage. Unfortunately, Grandpa could sometimes overdo it at the dinner table and end up with heartburn. Grandma would make him walk around the house to keep the blood moving so he could digest all that food, while she made him a nice, warm cup of tea from peppermint leaves she had grown in her garden. The peppermint soothed Grandpa's stomach, and pretty soon, he'd be ready for dessert.

SPELLING RELIEF: INDIGESTION

This condition is usually a stomach disorder, but may also relate to the small or large intestine. Symptoms include bloating, flatulence, abdominal pain, belching, a burning sensation or nausea. The problem may occur from consuming liquids with meals. This neutralizes enzymes that are needed to break down foods.

These herbs are useful in alleviating symptoms: mint, papaya, peppermint, chamomile and fennel. For inflammation of the colon, an enema using the herb slippery elm should provide fast relief.

Before The Burn

You may know that there are certain foods that always seem to irritate your stomach. Foods that are hard to digest, or foods that produce gas often cause stomach problems, or aggravate existing conditions. If you just can't resist, try taking an activated charcoal capsule along with the culprit food. Another option is to take one tablespoonful of olive oil before you eat. You may find that you can then enjoy hot or irritating foods without the discomfort.

If you like vegetables, but they don't like you, there's no need to despair. Just sprinkle fresh lemon juice on vegetables more than three hours before you plan to eat them. This marinade makes the veggies easier to digest. It also adds a nice flavor.

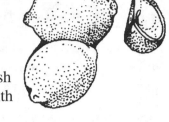

If you're going to serve a hard-to-digest meal, this side dish does double duty. Steam some zucchini and sprinkle with raw, grated almonds. It's tasty and will aid in digestion.

A Japanese radish called daikon is a wonderful digestive aid. It's crisp, refreshing and very effective, especially when eating oily or fried foods. You can add raw daikon to salads. Grate one or two tablespoons, or eat a few slices with your meal.

Here's a hot tip for indigestion sufferers: cayenne pepper. Sprinkle some (not too much) on all kinds of food and it will help in digestion.

Grandma's Brown Rice And Fresh Barley Belly Soup

A soup made from brown rice and fresh barley should help alleviate bloating and flatulence. Boil five parts water to one part of the grain mixture for ten to twelve minutes and then allow to simmer for forty-five minutes before straining. Allow to cool before consuming.

Natural Acid Neutralizers

Papaya is another natural cure for stomach pain. This tropical fruit has long been recognized for its qualities as a digestive aid. After eating, take papaya—you can drink papaya juice, eat the fresh fruit or take papaya pills. Most health food stores will carry a number of brands of papaya products to choose from. Check them out and see which works best for you.

For acid ingestion, you may find kelp tablets to be a welcome relief. Kelp is a form of seaweed which forms a gel that soothes upset stomachs by binding up stomach acid. A caution to those who must watch their salt intake: this is not the cure for you. Kelp (and other seaweed) is very high in sodium.

How about a spicy solution to your stomach ache? Try chewing cardamom seeds. This fragrant spice has long been recognized as a digestive aid. Chewing cardamom seeds can relieve nausea, discomfort and help to relieve gas buildup. Plus, it has a pleasant flavor. Other fragrant spices can be helpful too. Try anise seeds and caraway seeds. They'll help your stomach, and like the cardamom seeds, they can sweeten your breath.

If you suffer from acid indigestion, try chewing a teaspoon of dry rolled oats. Make sure you chew the oats thoroughly before you swallow. They will help to soothe you and neutralize the acid in your stomach.

Cookin' Up A Cure

This is a home remedy that may be a little difficult to take, but it really seems to work. At the first sign of stomach discomfort, boil one sliced onion in one cup of milk. Drink this while it's still warm. It's difficult, but it's better than the stomach pain.

Another way to neutralize acid is to drink raw potato juice. To make the juice, grate a potato and squeeze (it's best to squeeze through cheesecloth if you have it). One tablespoon diluted in half a cup of warm water should make you feel better. Be sure to drink it slowly.

Sometimes overeating can bring on a sensation known as a "sour stomach". Or, you may feel that something you've eaten "doesn't agree with you." Here's a quick remedy that many people find helpful for settling their stomach. Add one teaspoon of apple cider vinegar to a glass of water. If the sour taste is too much for you, you may want to add some honey.

Speaking of honey, this natural nectar has been found to bring sweet relief to some stomach pain sufferers. A tablespoon or two of honey can do wonders to relieve stomach cramps. This is no new-fangled remedy—the appreciation of honey's curative qualities dates all the way back to ancient Egypt.

Tartar For The Tummy

When I was a child, Grandma would give me cream of tartar in water whenever I had a stomach ache. She always had it on hand for baking and it always made me feel better (after a good belch or two).

To settle our stomachs, she would also make us arrowroot paste—arrowroot is terrific for settling the stomach. Make the paste by combining one tablespoon of arrowroot with enough water to get the right consistency. Mix until smooth. Then, boil, cool and add one tablespoon of fresh lime juice.

Without Sugar Or Spice

For stomach ailments, many doctors recommend the BRAT diet. This works particularly well if you have the stomach flu. It's a bland diet that consists of foods that are easy to take on an upset stomach: Bananas, Rice, Applesauce and Toast. Easy to remember, easy to digest.

Shower Yourself With Relief

Sometimes just a hot shower is all you need to feel better. Let the hot shower water run on your stomach. You should feel better—and more relaxed within ten to fifteen minutes.

WHEN THE ROOM IS SPINNING: MOTION SICKNESS

This order is caused by conflicting signals sent to the brain through the vestibule apparatus in the ear and sensory nerves.

Take four to five charcoal tablets approximately one hour before a trip. Ginger capsules are just as good, but you need to take two to three capsules one hour before the trip, then every three hours thereafter.

Motion Potions

If you get seasick, try taking marjoram tea. Drink a cup of tea before getting on board ship.

You can also try peppermint or chamomile tea. Both are excellent for soothing the stomach and relieving nausea.

Not quite so soothing a thought is this peppery drink. In a cup of warm water, mix an eighth teaspoon of cayenne pepper. Drink it all—you can hold your nose, if you like.

BELLY FLOPS: NAUSEA

If you're finding it difficult to eat, try peeling and eating half a cucumber. It will feel very soothing and refreshing and won't irritate your system.

Tummy Tonics

Fresh ginger or ginger capsules seem to reduce nausea and even eliminate it in many cases. In some countries, ginger powder is actually prescribed after surgery to alleviate the nausea from anesthesia.

Try placing a few drops of peppermint tincture under your tongue. The queasy feeling should go away in a few minutes. You can find a large variety of herbal tinctures at health food stores.

Peppermint tea is another herbal alternative to ease stomach discomfort. If you don't have the tea handy, try a peppermint candy.

Chamomile tea is a popular remedy for an upset stomach. There are many brands of chamomile tea that you can find in any grocery store or health food store. Chamomile tea is also very soothing and can help when you feel stress. It's great before bedtime, too. Note: if you are sensitive to ragweed, chrysanthemums or aster, you should avoid chamomile.

Yarrow tea can provide quick relief from nausea. Drink one cup when you start to get that queasy feeling. Cloves, cinnamon stick and ginger are all good for stopping nausea. Steep a couple of cloves in boiling water for five minutes, or try cinnamon stick, or one teaspoon of powdered ginger. Any one of these teas will help to ease your nausea.

From The Soda Fountain

Believe it or not, soda can help relieve nausea. Sipping ginger ale is a good preventive measure for nausea. You might also try Coca-Cola for an upset stomach. Cola syrup is also terrific for nausea. You can easily find this over-the-counter-item at your pharmacy. One teaspoon of this sweet syrup works very well.

Chewing on ice chips can also curb nausea.

Bumpy Ride Candy

Whenever we would travel long distances, Grandma always kept candies in her purse. Her favorite was barley sugar, and she always had a supply handy for long, bumpy rides. Any hard candy is a good deterrent for car sickness, but sugar always reminds me of Grandma. The best thing about this remedy is that if your kids get car sickness, you won't have to talk them into taking their medicine!

Managing Morning Sickness

Taking two or three capsules of powdered ginger root each morning can help you avoid morning sickness altogether.

Another morning sickness remedy is vitamin B-6. It is most effective for women who have severe morning sickness (vomiting several times a day). Check with your doctor before you start taking the vitamins because like many vitamins, taking too much B-6 can be harmful.

Nausea caused by morning sickness can often be allayed by eating crackers. Many women swear by saltines. Keep a box in the car, and even keep some in your purse. When that feeling comes over you, you'll be glad you have them handy.

If you suffer from morning sickness, you may get some relief from drinking one teaspoon of bicarbonate of soda in a half a glass of water. Or, try drinking carbonated mineral water.

A SORE SPOT: ULCERS

Ulcers may occur anywhere along the gastrointestinal tract, however, they are more common in the stomach when the stomach is unable to secrete sufficient quantities of mucous to protect the delicate lining from the hydrochloric acid.

Prevention is the key when it comes to ulcers. If you suffer from ulcer pain, avoiding the following foods could keep your suffering at bay: milk, fried foods, spicy foods, acidic foods and fatty foods. While these foods don't cause ulcers, avoiding them may keep you from getting a flare-up.

Although you should avoid spicy foods, cayenne pepper is a very helpful spice to use in ulcer healing. Drink an eighth teaspoon of cayenne pepper in a glass of water twice daily. If you can stand it, work your way up to a quarter teaspoon of the pepper.

A Dairy Don't

Never drink milk to soothe the stomach. The calcium in milk tends to stimulate the production of additional acid. The only milk that may be helpful is almond milk.

Soothing Stomach Savers

Ulcers respond well to a tea made from chamomile or bayberry. Cayenne capsules also tend to promote healing by increasing circulation.

Some people find that gingerroot can calm an ulcer flare-up. Licorice has been known to have the same effect. A variety known as DGL, deglycyrrhized licorice, is available in health food stores and can help protect the stomach's lining.

Drinking catnip tea before each meal can make a noticeable difference for many stomach ulcer sufferers. Either use a tea bag, or one teaspoon of catnip in a cup of boiling water. Let steep for five minutes, strain and drink.

Rejuvenate With Juice

Fresh cabbage juice will ease the problem but needs to be consumed immediately after juicing before oxidation has a chance to reduce its potency.

An extremely effective remedy is to take one tablespoon of aloe vera juice after each meal.

CHAPTER 10

HIS AND HERS

HOLDING YOUR NOSE: BODY ODOR

Perspiration is a natural bodily process and should not have an offensive odor. However, if the body needs a cleansing, the sweat glands may pick up toxins and odors from foods that are only partially digested. An herbal cleansing program is recommended in these cases.

From The Inside Out

Try taking zinc supplements, no more than fifteen milligrams a day without a doctor's supervision, to lessen body odor.

Clean out your insides to prevent unpleasant body odor. Fennel tea will do the trick nicely. Create the brew with a teaspoon of dried fennel and a cup of boiled water, steeping for five minutes before straining. Drink the tea first thing in the morning and later in the afternoon. You'll still sweat, but you won't smell a thing and neither will anyone else.

If you have to speak in public or you're going on a job interview and are worried about odor from nervous perspiration, try drinking sage tea. Use one and a half teaspoon of sage to a cup of boiling water, allowing it to set ten minutes before drinking. Drink this tea steadily throughout the day, right up to your big moment.

A Sprinkle A Day

Baking soda has been used for many years to combat body odor. Grandma always recommended it to mask unpleasant odors. The baking soda will last longer and be more effective if you make a paste by mixing it with a small amount of water. Placing a small amount in bath water also has an excellent odor controlling quality.

You may not go around craving a glass of fresh radish juice, but it can work wonders on stubborn body odor problems. You can use a juicer, food processor, or blender. It will take several bunches of radishes to make enough juice. Keep it in the refrigerator in a sealed jar. Use it the same way you would an underarm deodorant. You can do the same thing with fresh turnip juice.

Pickling Body Odor

The first time Grandma suggested using apple cider vinegar to relieve body odor, I was skeptical. Personally, I'd rather smell bad than smell like vinegar. But I knew she tended to be right about these things, so I agreed to try it. You don't have to take a bath in it for it to be effective; just dab on a little with a cotton ball. Fortunately, the vinegar smell soon fades, and you feel very clean. Vinegar kills off bacteria that can cause unpleasant odor.

Wash Away The Worry

If you've worked up a sweat digging in your garden or playing with your kids, try taking a warm, relaxing bath, adding a sock filled with fresh mint leaves. The pleasant aroma will relax you, and you'll come out smelling minty fresh.

Use a cucumber wash to deodorize your body naturally. Pick a big, juicy cucumber and cut it into four equal pieces. Rub the slices over the sweaty parts of your body and let your skin air dry. You'll feel fresh and clean as a daisy, and you'll smell just as good.

Dress For Success

According to Grandma, wearing natural fibers reduces the chance of body odor. Since people started dressing in more synthetic clothing, she swears that smelly perspiration problems have greatly increased. It's a fact that natural fibers, like cotton, allow air to circulate more easily, reducing sweating and the possibility of unpleasant body odor.

HERE TODAY, GONE TOMORROW: HAIR LOSS

A rinse of sage tea may stimulate hair growth. Saturate a small cloth with the tea and place on the affected areas for fifteen minutes at least four to five times a day.

THE END OF AN ERA: MENOPAUSE

Menopause refers to the point in a woman's life when she stops ovulating. Hormone levels drop and symptoms may include dizziness, headaches, hot flashes, depression and a reduced desire for sexual activity.

Give Your Body What It Needs

The body goes through many changes during menopause, and you may need to supplement your intake of vital nutrients. Make sure you eat a balanced diet. You may also need to take additional B-complex vitamins, calcium and magnesium.

To stop hot flashes, many women take a vitamin E supplement, from 400 to 1,200 milligrams daily, starting at a low dosage and gradually increasing it. You can also get your vitamin E in a multi-vitamin specifically for menopausal women. It's best to check with your doctor before starting a vitamin E regimen.

Restoring The Balance

The herb black cohosh has been used for hundreds of years to reduce the severity of symptoms and seems to have the ability to mimick the effects that estrogen would normally have.

Suma is an herb that is known for balancing hormones. You can buy this herb in capsule form at most health food stores. Follow the label directions.

A number of other herbs having an effect on the more common symptoms include ginseng, gota kola and dong quai.

Symptom- Reducing Regimens

Make Grandma's morning walk your own habit. Exercise can help reduce the severity of hot flashes or even eliminate them. It will also help ward off heart disease and osteoporosis, two ailments that strike women more commonly after menopause.

To help keep your body temperature at a normal level, drink plenty of water. Try to get eight glasses a day.

Try this breathing exercise to help you get through those hot flashes. Moderate your breathing so that you count to six while breathing in and count to six while breathing out. Breath this way ten times without taking a pause between breaths.

If you feel your face and neck getting flushed, grab an ice cube from the tray, and suck away. The flash will be gone in a flash.

THE MOODY BLUES: PREMENSTRUAL SYNDROME

PMS usually affects women seven to ten days before they begin menstruating. Symptoms are depression, cramps, headaches, breast tenderness, inability to have good sleep patterns, short tempers, and other personality changes.

You Are What You Eat

If you suffer from PMS, you may do well to alter your diet. Reducing your salt intake will help reduce the fluid retention that many women experience. This may be difficult for some, as cravings for salty foods is also a common PMS side-effect.

You may find that avoiding caffeine, sugar and alcohol will also make a difference. These substances are known to affect moods, so if you're prone to moodiness, try eliminating these from your diet (or cutting down)—you'll be pleased with the results.

Increasing calcium intake can be beneficial for easing premenstrual tension and for curbing menstrual cramps. Eat at least one portion of calcium rich foods each day. Some good examples of nutritious foods high in calcium are: leafy greens, including kale, parsley, endive and watercress; and beans, including chickpeas and lentils.

Many women have had success in limiting the effects of PMS by regularly taking B-6 vitamins or B-complex vitamins. Because it is possible to overdo it with vitamins, check with your doctor for his or her recommended dose.

Get A Move On

Many women find that exercise helps reduce many of the side-effects of PMS. Exercise is a vital component of a healthy lifestyle—exercising regularly can reduce stress and increase energy. Many women feel that making it a point to exercise during the week before the beginning of their menstrual cycle alleviates some of their moody swings, lethargy and general lack of energy.

The Herbalist's Checklist

The most effective herbs to alleviate symptoms are dong quai, raspberry leaves, and squaw vine. Either teas, tinctures, or capsules are available in most health food stores.

Chamomile tea is known to do wonders for nerves, so it only makes sense that this tea would be great for premenstrual tension. Make the tea several times throughout the day and sip your PMS away.

Taking two garlic tablets each day can relieve many of the symptoms of PMS including bloating, tender breasts and the blahs.

CHAPTER 11

IT'S ALL IN YOUR HEAD

ABOUT TO DROP: FATIGUE

Wake-Up Call

For those who live in the far north, it can be really hard to get out of bed on a cold winter's day. If you feel tired in the morning and have trouble getting yourself going, combine in a blender two tablespoons apple cider vinegar, one teaspoon honey, and a cup of warm water and blend thoroughly. Drink this liquid wake-up call every morning before breakfast. Within a few days, you should feel like an entirely new person.

If you're mentally exhausted, try this Austrian fatigue-fighter. In a bowl, mix together an unpeeled apple, cut into small pieces, and two cups of boiling water. Let it stand an hour, and then add a tablespoon of honey. Drink the sweetened apple water and eat the apple slices.

To increase your energy, drink a quart of this high power brew a day. Mix six ounces of cranberry juice, all-natural and unsweetened, two ounces of orange juice, and garnish with a fresh lime slice. Add some ice, stir to mix, and enjoy! You'll feel like an Olympic athlete in no time, or at the very least, you'll be able to get out of bed.

High-Energy Health Habits

"If you're tired, go to bed." That was Grandma's hard-to-argue-with logic. Fatigue is the body's natural signal that it needs rest, especially after strenuous physical activity. Take a load off, lie down on the sofa, or spend the day in bed.

On the other hand, too much of a good thing is bad. If you're resting a lot and still feel tired, you may need to get up and go for a walk instead. Grandma took her three-mile walk every morning. She always had plenty of energy and never had trouble sleeping at night.

If the fatigue is not related to an illness, it may be caused by a diet too high in fat and refined carbohydrates, both of which cause sluggishness. Increase your intake of whole grains and fresh fruits and vegetables.

Caffeine and sugar will give you a temporary boost, but you may feel more tired than ever after the effects wear off. To combat that tired feeling from three to five o'clock in the afternoon, make the transition to a caffeine-free life and reduce your sugar intake. After you get used to it, you should feel better than ever.

Vital Herbs

Cayenne increases circulation and may boost energy levels. It may be taken in capsule form. Other useful herbs are ginseng, guarana and gingko biloba.

Revive And Refresh

You know how a hot shower gets you going in the morning? Try a bath or shower to revive whenever you're fatigued. The water will help you feel relaxed and refreshed. In hot weather, cool off by misting yourself with water or splashing cool water on your face.

Nothing could get me out of a deep sleep faster than the smell of bacon frying in Grandma's kitchen. Certain scents seem to have an invigorating effect. Try adding essential oils to your bath, such as peppermint, lavender, or rosemary. For a real kickstart, use a handful of rosemary leaves and lemon rind.

If you find yourself drifting off and need a quick pick-me-up, try this circulation boosting exercise. Press your elbows into your sides or your knees together. It will wake you up, get your blood moving, and make you more mentally alert.

IN OVERDRIVE: HYPERACTIVITY

Hyperactivity has been linked to a disorder of the central nervous system. Symptoms manifest as a lack of concentration, temper tantrums, sleep disorders, and getting easily frustrated when performing a task, among others. It may be linked to artificial preservatives and sweeteners, high consumption of refined carbo-hydrates, wheat, soft drinks and chocolate.

Take valerian root extract and use according to provided instructions. Valerian root may also be taken in capsule form.

SEARCHING FOR THE SANDMAN: INSOMNIA

Sleeplessness is a serious problem, but it should respond to simple solutions. It may be caused by a variety of drugs, low blood sugar, asthma, stress, or even a lack of certain minerals such as calcium and magnesium.

Sweet Dreams Diet Plan

The mineral magnesium, with its muscle relaxing properties, can help you get to sleep more readily. Two hours before bedtime, take 400 milligrams of magnesium, along with 50 milligrams of vitamin B6 to facilitate the body's use of magnesium. Of course, you should always check with your doctor before taking any supplements.

Eating lots of lettuce late in the evening may help you get a more restful night's sleep. But, be aware that lettuce acts as a diuretic, so while it may relax you so you can fall asleep, it may also wake you so you can go to the bathroom.

Eliminating salt from your evening meal can help prevent sleeplessness. So can cutting out after-dinner snacks. In fact, it is recommended that you have your last meal several hours before you turn in for the night.

Goat's milk has been known to help some insomniacs get some zzzzs. Try drinking six ounces of goat's milk before each meal and another six ounces before bedtime. Some people have reported a better night's sleep within a week. Goat's milk is available in some health food stores.

Rest For The Weary

This is a remedy for insomnia that has a host of excellent side effects. Exercise. Be sure to exercise regularly but be sure to workout during the day—never before bedtime. The extra energy will just keep you awake.

If you have young children, you know how letting them run around like crazy, playing as hard as they can during the day, tires them out so they can get a good night's sleep. We're not so different from our kids. Getting exercise or doing hard physical work will wear you out, and you'll have no problem drifting off.

Grandma always stretched and did her deep breathing exercises before turning in for the night. It was part of her usual routine. Stretching aids circulation which promotes restfulness. Concentrate on slowing down your breath to help you relax.

Bedtime Rituals

Grandma always said counting sheep just made the sheep tired. Here's a remedy for the rest of us who don't feel like jumping over fences all night long. Try taking a warm bath in the evening. Add some aromatic oils that you can buy in a health food store. Many boutiques also sell aromatherapy oils. Make sure you buy the kind that are good for relaxation. While soaking, sip some herbal tea such as chamomile, ginger or Celestial Seasoning's Sleepy Time Tea. You might also try reading a book or lighting some candles. You should feel relaxed (and pampered). Make sure you head right to bed, and snuggle in for a good night's sleep.

One home remedy that just about everyone has heard of is warm milk. It's been around forever, and there's a good reason: it works. Grandma swore by this. She would enjoy a cup of warm milk almost every night. And, like everything else she did, Grandma would jazz it up a bit. She would add honey to taste (about one or two teaspoons should do) and a half teaspoon of nutmeg. Then, she would sit quietly and sip, relax and enjoy.

Remember how hard it was to keep your eyes open in math class in the late afternoon? Or how riding in a car or on a train will put you right out? If you have a hard time falling asleep, try boring yourself into unconsciousness. Read a book before turning in or recite a poem in your head, whatever will distract you from thinking about how much you want to go to sleep and how badly you need the rest. These relaxing pastimes should help relax you and lull you to sleep.

Snuggling Up

If you love animals, try having your pets sleep in the same bed with you. It's been shown that pets help people relax and can actually lower blood pressure. If you wake up in the middle of the night and have trouble getting back to sleep, pet your cat or dog. It will quiet you and hopefully make you feel drowsy again.

Calm In A Cup

The most effective herb is valerian root, taken in capsule form or as a tea. Certain foods that have a high level of tryptophan promote sleep. They include tuna, bananas, turkey and dates. This is why you get tired after Thanksgiving dinner.

The herbs passionflower and hops help reduce anxieties and tension that may prevent you from getting a good night's sleep. Take these herbs powdered in capsules or brew into a tea. To a lesser degree, chamomile and sage also act as sleep aids. Use these remedies to help with occasional sleeplessness. You should not rely upon them to help you fall asleep on a regular basis.

The Better Part Of Valor

Sometimes the best answer is just not to fight it. If you can't sleep, get up and do something. Pay bills, catch up on paperwork or letterwriting, find out what's showing on the late show. You will sleep when you get tired enough. Usually a couple of days as a night owl is enough to cure sleeplessness.

IQ INVASION: MEMORY PROBLEMS

Food For Thought

Diets that are high in processed low nutrition foods tend to cause a reduction in mental powers. Consume more natural raw foods, especially whole grains high in Vitamin B.

Deficiency of Vitamin B12 has been linked to nervous system problems and impairment of mental facilities. Older people are especially prone to this vitamin deficiency. Check with your doctor to see if this may be a problem for you and what an appropriate dosage is.

Eating raw almonds each day can help to improve your memory. Nuts are very high in fat, so only a few (five or six) should do the trick. Sunflower seeds can do the trick, too. Just a handful a day is all you'll need.

Same Time, Same Place

Memory is context specific. Clinical studies have shown that college students who study in the same place and at the same time of day that an exam is given do significantly better than those who study elsewhere and at other times of day. If you learn something in a particular environment, returning to those conditions makes it easier to remember.

You can put the psychologists' research to work in your own life. If you're studying for a test or just trying to keep a grip on what you have to do this week, try adding a scent to it. Study or go over your schedule while breathing in a distinctive fragrance—lavender, cinnamon, rosemary, or anything else that appeals to you. Whenever you need to jolt your memory, take a whiff of the scent.

Rescue Your Recall

The herb gota kola and ginkgo biloba have been used to increase memory effectiveness for hundreds of years. You should be able to find capsules at your local health food store.

An herb called yerba mate has a lot of fans who claim that among other fine qualities, this herb helps to increase memory. Try it for yourself. Drink one cup each morning. But, be aware that unlike most herb teas, this one contains caffeine (although it does contain less caffeine than coffee).

Eyebright tea can boost your memory. To one and a half cups of boiling water add a half ounce of eyebright and one tablespoon of clover honey. Let steep until cool. Strain and put in a container. Drink three quarters cup of the tea before lunch and dinner.

Make sage tea and add three or four cloves. This combination is supposed to strengthen the memory. You can drink this tea once a day.

Picking Up The Scent

Why not try aromatherapy to improve your memory? Smelling crushed caraway seeds can help sharpen your recollection. You can also try ground cloves or coriander seeds.

BRIGHT-EYED AND BUSHY-TAILED: MENTAL ALERTNESS

For physical as well as mental energy, try bee pollen. After breakfast, take one teaspoon of granular pollen, or if you prefer, take two 500 mg pollen pills. Many people notice a difference in alertness and memory within weeks of first taking the pollen.

Another very effective method of increasing mental alertness and improving memory is to consume one to two teaspoons of Brazil nut powder in a cup of juice. There are specific amino acids that stimulate brain function found in the Brazil nut.

What Did You Say That Cure Was?

Whenever someone in my family had a problem remembering, Grandma would go looking for a fresh artichoke. She would pull the artichoke leaves off and place them into a jar with just enough water to cover the leaves. She would then place the jar in a pan of water and bring it to a boil allowing the jar to remain in the boiling water for at least two hours. As the water boiled away, she kept adding more so that the boiling water was up to the level of the solution in the jar. She would then strain the contents and squeeze the leaves until all the liquid was removed. She would then have the forgetful one take three tablespoons of this artichoke broth, three to four times a day for five days. Once again, Grandma knew best: Studies have shown that artichoke leaves contain substances similar in nature to caffeine.

BYE, BYE BUTTERFLIES: NERVOUSNESS

Kiss It Goodbye

If you are prone to nervousness, you should cut caffeine out of your diet. Besides tea, coffee and colas, you should avoid chocolate. Substitute herbal teas for the caffeinated beverages and carob for chocolate. Carob is available in many varieties in health food stores. It has the consistency of chocolate and is used in all of the same ways. Carob treats should curb your chocolate craving without adding caffeine to your diet.

Tranquilizing Tonics

The remedy for nervousness and hyperactivity are basically the same, celery juice. Both the stalk and the seeds of celery contain the substance "phthalide." Since raw celery juice is not very appealing, you might want to add a small amount of honey to sweeten it. Consume a quarter cup daily for about three days to solve the problem. Celery juice has also been used successfully to lower blood pressure.

Drink sage tea three times a day. You can buy sage tea bags at your health food store. If you prefer to use dry herbs, use one teaspoon to one cup of warm water. Let steep for several minutes.

Foods That Fight Stress

A seaweed called kombu is said to make an excellent tea for nerves. Kombu and other seaweed is readily available at health food stores. In a quart of water, boil a three-inch strip of the kombu for ten minutes. Drink the tea throughout the day in a half cup portions.

Onions are said to have a relaxing quality. Finely chop one large onion into tiny pieces and mix in one tablespoon of honey. Eat half of the onion mixture with lunch, and half with dinner.

If you have a sudden stressful situation occur, try eating a handful of sesame seeds. They're rich in calcium and can help you get through the emotional episode.

Eating strawberries in season can calm your nerves. Just a few berries after each meal is a great, relaxing treat.

Kicking Back

Try taking a relaxing Epsom salt bath—Grandma swore by them. Pour two cups of Epsom salt into your warm bath. Soak for half an hour and feel the tension drain from you. Dim the lights for even more relaxation.

Listening to calming music may just do the trick, especially if your tension stems from a difficult day at the office. You might try combining this with the cure above and bring the radio into the bathroom.

FORGET ME NOT: SENILITY

This lessening of mental powers and memory often occurs in the elderly, and may be caused by the increase in medications taken by this age group.

The herb gingko biloba has been used effectively in capsule form as well as gota kola. A combination of blue cohosh and anise has also been effective.

THE END OF YOUR ROPE: STRESS

Valerian root capsules have produced excellent results in reducing stress and anxiety levels. Teas made from chamomile and pau d'arco are also very effective.

Low Stress Lifestyle

One of the simplest answers to stress is something my grandmother always said: "Take time to enjoy life!" Have more fun, whatever that means for you. Get out of the house and get some exercise, a quieting walk like my grandmother enjoyed. Pet owners are less likely to suffer from stress-related disorders, so consider adopting a cat or dog. Take time every day for yourself, to meditate or nap or just have a few quiet moments alone.

A number of foods tend to aggravate a stressful condition and should be avoided. These include sugars, fried foods, colas, products containing white flour and potato chips.

When You're Under The Gun

When anxiety attacks, focus on your breathing, slowing it down, inhaling more deeply, and exhaling fully. It will help calm down other stress symptoms, such as racing heart beat and tense muscles.

Traditional healing recognizes the ability of certain scents to effect changes in the body. Using essential oils like lavender, rosemary, and pine in your bath can help relax muscles and relieve stress. Try putting pots of apple-cinnamon potpourri around your house to make your home a low-stress zone.

When you're feeling pressure, think acupressure. Massage the webbed area on your left hand between the thumb and index finger. Really work on it, kneading for five minutes—it will probably hurt. After a while, you'll notice that the pain will decrease, and so will your tension.

Draw yourself a warm bath, add some bubbles, and settle in for a long soak. Create a sensual get-away for yourself by lighting candles and playing soothing music. Use your imagination to leave worries behind you. Picture yourself on a tropical island, floating in warm, clear, blue-green water. By the time you get out of the tub, you won't remember why you were stressed out in the first place.

CHAPTER 12

ASSORTED HINTS AND TIPS

A SUB FROM A CEREAL BOX

The lining paper from cereal boxes make a great substitute for waxed paper.

THE BACTERIA SPONGE

Once a week, throw the sponge into the dishwasher to sterilize it and kill all the bacteria.

SOMETHING TO CUDDLE UP WITH

A large one liter plastic soda bottle can make an excellent hot water bottle in an emergency. Make sure you wrap it in a hand towel before you apply it to your skin.

A FOREIGN PROBLEM

Dinnerware being imported from foreign countries may still contain traces of lead and other heavy metals. Salad dressings that contain a mild acid such as vinegar and even tomatoes may be strong enough to release these metals.

SHAKE IT BABY

To remove an unsightly residue buildup from inside a flower vase or wine bottle, try using a solution of 2 tablespoons of salt, some raw rice, and 1 cup of white vinegar and shake vigorously.

DECAL BEGONE

Transparent decals may be easily removed using a solution of lukewarm water and $\frac{1}{4}$ cup of white vinegar. Place the solution on a sponge and dampen the area thoroughly for a few minutes. If this doesn't work saturate the decal and allow it to stand for 15 minutes then try again with very hot water.

COVER UP

To cover a scratch on your refrigerator or freezer, try using the same color enamel paint. This really works great and will last a long time.

KEEP DUST OFF THE TV AND COMPUTER SCREENS

A used dryer sheet can be used to clean the screens and the screens will not attract dust.

HOW DOES ALKA-SELTZER®, WORK?

Alka-Seltzer® contains citric acid and baking soda and when they hit the water the acid and base mix and fizz up. This similar to the volcano trick, when you add vinegar to the baking soda and it fizzed and foamed up over the top of the volcano.

POP, POP, FIZZ, FIZZ ALKA-SELTZER® WILL CLEAN TOILETS

Just drop 2-3 Alka-Seltzer® tablets in your toilet and wait 20 minutes before scrubbing with a toilet brush. Between the citric acid and the bubbles it will work great.

GREASE REMOVER

To clean your can opener, try running a piece of paper towel through it. This will pick up the grease and some of the gunk.

GET THE STINK OUT OF GASOLINE

To deodorize gasoline, just add 20 drops of sassafras oil to every gallon or solvent.

STREAKER

If the sun is shining on your windows, try not to wash them until they are in the shade. When they dry too fast they tend to show streaks.

PERMANENT MARKER STAINS ON COUNTER

Just use rubbing alcohol on a piece of paper towel.

STOP DUST FROM SETTLING ON ARTIFICIAL FLOWERS

Just lightly spray the flowers with hair spray.

PUT A LID ON IT

A fire in a pan can easily be put out by just placing a lid over the fire, thus cutting off the oxygen supply.

ALCOHOL TO THE RESCUE

Black soot marks on candles are unsightly and can be removed with rubbing alcohol.

BE GENTLE

A nick on the rim of a glass can be easily removed with an emery board. Don't use a nail file or sandpaper. They are too coarse and will scratch the glass and ruin it.

PASS ME THE PEANUT BUTTER, HOLD THE HAIR

One of the best methods of removing chewing gum from a child's hair is to use a small amount of non-chunky peanut butter (not the natural kind). Other methods such as placing the person's head in the freezer for 45 minutes is not recommended.

LEATHER REVIVAL

If you want to revive the beauty of leather, try beating two egg whites lightly, then applying the mixture to the leather with a soft sponge. Allow it to remain on for 3-5 minutes before cleaning off with a soft cloth, just dampened with clear warm water. Dry immediately and buff off any residues.

SAVING STEEL WOOL PADS

Since used steel wool pads rust easily, just store them in a plastic bag in the freezer and they can be reused.

ODOR EATERS

A number of foods are capable of removing odors. Vanilla extract placed in a bottle top in the refrigerator will remove odors, while dry mustard is commonly used to eliminate onion odors from hands and cutting boards.

KILL REFRIGERATOR ODORS

Place a cotton ball with a small amount of vanilla on it in the refrigerator.

ON A CLEAR DAY

To prevent windows from steaming up, rub then with equal amounts of glycerin and methyl alcohol. This combination will neutralize the buildup of minor condensation.

I WONDER WHERE THE YELLOW WENT

Stale milk will do a great job of cleaning plant leaves. The protein "casein" has a mild cleansing effect on the plant cell walls.

A SALAD SOLUTION

If you run out of wood oil, try using mayonnaise. A very, light coating rubbed into the wood will help protect the finish. It should be rubbed in well and be sure not to leave a residue. Leftover tea is a beverage that can be used on wood furniture and also to clean varnished furniture.

POURING SALT ON AN OPEN SPILL

If you ever spill red wine on you're carpet, try pouring salt on the area as soon as possible and watch the wine being absorbed almost instantly, then wait until it dries, and vacuum it up. Salt tends to provide a special capillary action that will attract most liquids.

SHAKE IT BABY, SHAKE IT

If you wish to make a unique salad dressing just place a small amount of olive oil and wine vinegar inside an almost empty ketchup bottle and shake.

MONEY SAVER

Don't bother buying fancy dust, cloths that are treated to attract dust when all you have to do is to dip a piece of cheesecloth in a mixture of 2 cups of water and $\frac{1}{4}$ cup of lemon oil. Allow the cheesecloth to air dry and it will do just as good as the expensive: cloth.

BEATS IRONING

If you want your sheer curtains to come out of the washing machine "wrinkle-free," just dissolve a package of unflavored gelatin in a cup of boiling water and add it to the final rinse. The protein has a relaxing, or softening effect on the fabric.

LEMON TREE, VERY USEFUL

For a brighter shoe, shine, place a few drops of lemon juice on your shoes when you are polishing them. Also, a small amount of lemon juice mixed with salt will remove mold and mildew from most surfaces. The juice is just acidic enough to do the job.

REMOVE TAR FROM HANDS

If you rub vegetable oil on your hands and allow it to remain for a few minutes, it will remove tar.

DRIVEWAY CLEANER

Try using powdered laundry detergent to clean the driveway.

TRY IT, YOU WILL BECOME A BELIEVER

If you want to remove glue residue on almost any surface, try using vegetable oil on a rag. Residue from sticky labels are also a breeze to remove. The vegetable oil tends to neutralize the glues bonds.

A GIRL'S BEST FRIEND

All diamonds and gold jewelry can easily be cleaned by mixing a solution of 50/50 white vinegar and warm water. Dip a soft toothbrush into the solution and brush gently. Opals, emeralds, and pearls are too delicate for this type of treatment. Costume jewelry should only be cleaned with a weak solution of baking soda and water to avoid damaging the glue bonds. You can also drop 2 Alka-Seltzer® tablets into a glass of tap water and place the jewelry in for 2-3 minutes.

EXTINGUISHING THE OLD FLAME

One of the best fire extinguishers is baking soda. The oxygen supply is cut off and the flame goes right out. Always keep an open box in the cupboard next to the range.

TOILET ODORS

Place a box of baking soda behind the toilet to eliminate the odors.

A POPPER OUTER

Tough nut and bolts are easy to remove after you pour some cola or other carbonated water on them and allow them to sit for about 20 minutes. The mild acidic action of either citric or phosphoric acid will usually do the job.

NEUTRALIZE ME

The acid around a battery post can easily be cleaned with a thick solution of baking soda and water. Allow it to soak for 10-15 minutes before washing it off. Baking soda is a mild base and will neutralize the weak acid.

SMILE!

A method of cleaning dentures that works as well as the expensive spreads is to just soak them overnight in white vinegar.

TO ELIMINATE ODORS IN THE SINK

Just add $1/4$ cup of lemon juice to the dishwater.

RING AROUND THE TABLE

When you place a glass with a wet bottom on wood furniture the water may react with the stain in the wood or whatever wax was used leaving a white ring. These rings may be removed by mixing a small amount of salt with 2 tablespoons of vegetable oil. Apply the solution and allow it to stand for at least 1 hour before rubbing the area gently. Baking soda may be substituted for salt if a less abrasive mixture is desired for more delicate surfaces.

A NUTTY SOLUTION

The broken edges of nuts can be rubbed gently on wood furniture to mask scratches. Just find a nut that matches the color and the results will surprise you. The most common ones are pecans, walnuts, and hazelnuts.

IT REALLY HITS THE SPOT

If you are going to wash a load of greasy clothes, try adding a bottle of cola to the load. It will really improve the cleaning action of most detergents. Colas contain a weak acid that will help to dissolve the grease. Cola can also be used to clean the rings off toilets.

FILL 'ER UP

A trick used by antique dealers to remove hairline cracks on china plates or cups is to simmer the cup in milk for 45 minutes. Depending on the size of the crack the protein (casein) in the milk will fill in the crack.

BUG SLIDE

Oven Guard or spraying vegetable oil on a clean car bumper before a trip will make it easy to remove the bugs when you return.

GREAT, GRATER TIP

Cleaning the grater will never be a problem if you use a small piece of raw potato before trying to wash it out. Sometimes a toothbrush comes in handy too.

GREASE CUTTER

If you are expecting to have a problem with a real greasy pan, try placing a few drops of ammonia in the pan with your soap, suds.

ELIMINATING TARNISH

Line a shallow pan with aluminum foil and then add 1 tablespoon of baking soda for every 2 cups of water and heat the pan to 150ºF. Lay the silverware in the pan making sure that it touches the aluminum foil and the stains will disappear.

SLOWING DOWN TARNISH

If you place a small piece of chalk in a silver chest it will absorb moisture and slow tarnishing. Calcium carbonate (chalk) absorbs moisture very slowly from the air. If you break the chalk up and expose the rough surface it will be more efficient.

BAG 'EM, DANO

A great idea used by professional cooks worldwide is to keep a small plastic baggie handy in case you have both hands in a food dish or dough and need to answer the telephone.

LUCKY FOR YOU

If you have ever wondered why you can place your hand into a hot oven and not be burned, the answer is simple, air does not conduct heat well. However, if you leave it in there long enough it will come out medium-well. Water conducts heat more efficiently and will easily burn you.

MESSY!

The glue on any type of contact paper will easily melt by running a warm iron over it or using a hair dryer on high heat.

SPRINKLE, SPRINKLE

If you want to sharpen up your carpet colors, try sprinkling a small amount of salt around. The salt provides a mild abrasive cleaning action that won't hurt the fibers.

ROUND AND ROUND WE GO

Have you ever wondered how to efficiently get the last drop of ketchup out of the bottle? All you have to is to hold the neck of the bottle, then swing the bottle in a circular motion from your side and hold on tight!

REMOVING ODORS

To remove refrigerator odors, try leaving a small cup of used coffee grounds on 2 shelves. An excellent method of removing odors from the kitchen is to keep a few washed charcoal briquettes in a shallow dish on top of the refrigerator. Frying a small amount of cinnamon will chase all odors from the home.

VERY UPLIFTING

An easy method of raising the nap of a carpet after a piece of furniture has matted it down is to place an ice cube on the matted down area overnight.

MEASURING UP

If you want to use the fewest utensils possible, first measure out all the dry ingredients then the wet ingredients. By doing this you can use the measuring spoons or cups for double-duty.

SMART MOVE

Used microwave food containers should be saved and used for leftovers, just fill, freeze, and re-heat. It is always wise to check and see if a dish is microwave safe and will not melt. Just place the container next to a $1/2$ full cup of water and turn the microwave on high for about $1^{1}/_{2}$-minutes or until the water is boiling. If the dish is hot when you touch it, you will be able to cook with it.

SLIPPERY SUBJECT

When preparing a pan that needs to be greased, try saving your salt-free butter wrappers or use a fresh piece of bread. Remember salt butter wrappers may cause foods to stick.

DON'T BURST YOUR BUBBLE

An easy solution for children to use when blowing bubbles is to mix 1 tablespoon of glycerin with 2 tablespoons of a powdered laundry detergent in 1 cup of warm water. Any unpainted piece of metal can easily be shaped with a circle on one end to use with the solution. Blowing into the mixture with a straw will also cause smaller bubbles to float up. If you want colored bubbles add food coloring.

ONE FOR THE GRIPPER

If your glasses are slick, try placing a wide rubber band on them for so that the children will get a better grip.

SAVES ON THE WASHING

Ice cream cones are notorious for leaking ice cream. To solve this problem, just place a standard size or miniature marshmallow on the bottom of the inside of the cone to act as a plug.

REAL MILK SHAKE

Since fresh milk is difficult to transport on a road trip and young children require their milk, bring along some powdered dry milk and just add water and shake, a treat fit for a child.

COMING UNGLUED

Plastic wrap loves to hug itself. If you hate this problem just keep the package in the refrigerator. The cold keeps it from sticking together.

SALVAGE JOB

If you accidentally burn or scorch a food, place the pot or dish immediately into cold water. This will stop the cooking action so that the balance of the food will not be affected. The damaged food must them be discarded and a fresh piece of white bread placed on top of the rest of the food for a short period while the food is reheated to remove the burnt odor.

CRUMMY SOLUTION

Too much mayonnaise or salad dressing can ruin a dish. To fix the problem, try adding bread, crumbs to absorb the excess.

REVIVAL

Almost any soft rubber ball including tennis balls can be brought back to life and the bounce returned by leaving the balls in an oven with only the pilot light overnight. This will cause expansion of the air inside the ball.

COOL IDEA

If you wish to cool a hot dish more rapidly, try placing the dish or pot into a pan of cold salted water. The salt will lower the temperature of the water even more.

SUMMERTIME

To keep salt free flowing in a humid climate, just add some raw rice to the shaker to absorb the moisture. Rice absorbs moisture very slowly under these conditions and lasts for a long time.

ICE, CUBE STORAGE

Large sugar and flour bags can be used to store ice cubes. They are much thicker than plastic bags. Rubbing a clean, lightly dampened dishrag on the inside of the bag will remove any sugar granules that might still be lurking about.

EATABLE CANDLE HOLDER

Natural candle holders can be made from small marshmallows. If they are kept refrigerated they will work better.

CLEAN LIVING

If you have a problem with mildew forming in your refrigerator, just spray the inside with vegetable oil. Spray the freezer after it has been defrosted and next time it will be easier to defrost.

PUT ON A THIN COAT

To keep your blender and mixer working great, be sure and lubricate all moving parts with a very light coating of mineral oil (not vegetable oil). This should be done every 3 months. Before you use a measuring cup to measure a sticky liquid, try spraying the inside with vegetable oil and the liquid will flow more freely.

SLICK IDEA

If you have a problem with ice cube trays sticking to the bottom of the shelf, try placing a piece of waxed paper under the tray. Freezing temperatures do not affect waxed paper.

FREEZER MELT

A common icemaker problem is freeze-ups. Next time this happens just use the hair dryer to defrost the problem. This problem won't occur if you release a few ice cubes every few days.

WORKS LIKE MAGIC

Have you ever stuck two glasses together and couldn't get them apart? Next time it happens just fill the top glass with ice water and then place the bottom one in a few inches of hot tap water in the sink. Should only take a few seconds.

GETTING IN SHAPE

Butcher blocks will not only harbor bacteria deep down in the cracks but are also difficult to clean. They need to be washed with a mild detergent, then dried thoroughly and covered with a light layer of salt to draw any moisture that may have gotten into the crevices. The wood can then be treated with a very light coating of mineral oil. Make sure it is only a light coating since mineral oil may affect the potency of a number of vitamins in fruits and vegetables.

TIME SAVER

Keeping a grater clean so that you can continue to work and still grate a number of different foods is an old chef's secret. A chef will always grate the softest items first, them grate the firmer ones.

COMING UNGLUED

At one time or another we have all experienced the problem of postage stamps that have stuck together. Next time this happens just place the stamps in the freezer for about 10 minutes.

THRIFTY IDEA

Dishwasher soap can be expensive. If you want to save money just purchase the least expensive one and add 2 teaspoons of white vinegar to the dishwasher. You dishes will come out spot-free.

BEGONE BUMPER STICKER

Allow white vinegar to soak into the sticker for 1 hour before scraping off.

KEEP WINDSHIELDS FROM DEVELOPING FROST

If you want to keep your windshields from developing frost at night, just rub a slice of raw onion on the windshield. The onion juice will do the job.

HUNDREDS OF YEARS OLD

Headaches may be relieved by taking the herb "Feverfew."

CAN PROTECTION

The lids from 1-pound coffee cans will fit a can of opened motor oil and stop the dust or debris from contaminating it.

LOCKS, NOT LOX

A hairdryer will defrost your automobile locks in the winter.

SCRATCH REMOVER

A small amount of toothpaste on a cloth will remove minor scratches on automobile finishes.

YUCH! BIRD DROPPINGS

To remove bird dropping safely from a car finish, just use carbonated water.

GETTING BACK ON SOLID GROUND

If you get stuck in snow or mud, try using your car floor mat or a blanket kept in the trunk for traction.

A BIT CHILLY

If you run your air conditioner for 4-6 minutes during the winter it will keep the seals in good shape for the summer.

NO NIPPING, IT'S POISON

If your windshield wipers are smearing the windows, try wiping them with rubbing alcohol.

LET THERE BE LIGHT

Used milk containers can be filled with old candle wax and kept in the car for emergencies. Place a long candle in the center for the wick. It will burn for hours.

TRY SODIUM PHOSPHATE

TSP will remove grease stains from concrete after you scrape off the excess.

RUB-A-DUB-DUB

To prevent the rubber around your car doors from freezing, try rubbing the rubber moldings with vegetable oil.

BE GENTLE

Steel wool pads make an excellent white wall cleaner. Best to use as fine a steel wool pad as you can find.

THE ½ GALLON SIZE

Old milk cartons make excellent sand containers if you're stuck on ice.

TO THE SEAT OF THE PROBLEM

If you place a sheet of fabric softener under your car seat it will keep your car smelling fresh. Cleaning it out will help too.

CHURCH KEY TO THE RESCUE

When you can't open a jar, try placing it in a sink with a few inches of hot tap water for about 10 minutes; then try again. If this doesn't work use an old type bottle opener and place the pointed tip under the lid and gently pry the cap away. Do this gently all around the top and it should release enough pressure to allow you to open it.

CHAPTER 13

PERSONAL GROOMING FACTS

THIS WILL REALLY GIVE YOUR SHAMPOO A LIFT

If you want your hair to be shiny, just add a small amount of vodka to the shampoo bottle.

SLIPPERY WHEN WET?

For inexpensive bath oil, try using sunflower oil and either lavender or rose petal herb.

A REVIVAL

Hairbrushes and combs may be revived by soaking them in a pot of warm water and 1 tablespoon of baking soda or ammonia.

REFLECTING

If you lose a contact lens, turn the lights off and use a flashlight, the lens will reflect the light.

SQUEAKY CLEAN

If you want your hair to really sparkle, try adding a teaspoon of white vinegar to your final rinse.

RING AROUND THE FINGER

If you are unable to remove a ring, try placing your hand in a bowl of very cold water for a few seconds.

OR JUST WEAR GLOVES

If you would like to keep dirt from getting under your nails when you are working in the garden, just rub your nails over a bar of soap before starting work.

A CLEANER-UPPER

Laundry detergent makes an excellent hand cleaner for very hard to clean hands.

A CUP OF JOE

If you have red hair or are a brunette, try rinsing your hair with black coffee, then clear water to add luster.

FEET ADE

If you want to freshen your feet, try using a few fresh lemon slices. Just rub them in.

THIS WILL SNAP YOU AWAKE INSTANTLY

The life of pantyhose can be extended if they are placed in the freezer for the first night only. It will strengthen the fibers, but make sure you thaw them out before wearing then, unless you are having trouble waking up in the morning.

TASTES GOOD TOO

An inexpensive facial treatment is as follows: for normal to somewhat oily skin, use 1 cup of yogurt, 1 teaspoon of fresh lemon juice, 1 teaspoon of fresh orange juice, and 1 teaspoon of carrot juice. Blend all ingredients well and apply to your face for 10-15 minutes then rinse with warm water.

NEW USE FOR BREAKFAST FOOD

For a great facial scrub, try using a paste of oatmeal and water. Apply the paste then allow it to dry until your skin feels tight. Then remove it with your fingers with a back and forth motion to remove the dead skin.

ODE DE REFRIGERATOR

Perfume should be stored in the refrigerator if your not going to use it up over a reasonable period of time, approximately 30 days.

GREAT FOR HALLOWEEN

A great facial can be had by mashing $\frac{1}{2}$ avocado and spreading it thickly on your face. Wait 20 minutes: then wash off with warm water. Don't let your husband see you.

WHY DIDN'T I THINK OF THAT

Place a small amount of vegetable oil on the threads of nail polish bottles and the lid won't stick.

YUK!

To make your own deodorant, mix 2 teaspoons of baking soda, 2 teaspoons of petroleum jelly, and 2 teaspoons of talcum powder.

FRUIT-PASTE

To remove the yellow from your teeth, try using mashed fresh strawberries to brush with.

A LITTLE DAB WILL DO YA

Many toothpastes are now adding baking soda to their formula. However, you could just use a small amount of baking soda to brush your teeth. Just dampen your brush and sprinkle it on.

A PASTY

For bad sunburn, try making a paste of baking soda and water, works almost as good as the white vinegar.

HOW DRY I AM

If you want to make a bar of soap last longer, try, unwrapping it before you use it and allow it to dry out.

SHAMPOO AWAY

To add shine to your hair and to remove shampoo buildup, try adding 2 table-spoons of apple cider vinegar to the rinse water.

A LITTLE ACID GOES A LONG WAY

Before polishing your nails, try applying a small amount of white vinegar to your nails. They will stay shiny longer and it will clean them. Bleaching your fingernails is easy. All you have to do is soak them in lemon or lime juice. The mild citric acid will do the job.

CLEAN BATHROOM WALLS AND FINGERNAILS

Mix ¼ cup of white vinegar and ¼ cup of baking soda in 1 gallon of warm water. This solution will do a great job on your bathroom walls and keep your fingernails white as well as being harmless.

BABY YOURSELF

Baby oil will do the same job as a fancy cleansing cream at about a third of the price.

THE EYES HAVE IT

For puffy eyes, place slices of cucumber on your eyes. There is a chemical in cucumber that acts as an anti-inflammatory.

PERFUME HOLDER

If you want your perfume to last longer, try applying a small amount of petroleum jelly first on the area.

SKINADE

Skin blemishes can be cleared up quickly by dabbing them with lemon juice 4-6 times per day.

BALANCING ACT

If you want to restore the natural acid balance to your skin, try using $\frac{1}{2}$ cup of apple cider vinegar in a basin of water. Splash it on your face the allow it to dry before removing with a towel.

BEING THRIFTY

To make an inexpensive shampoo mix $\frac{1}{2}$ cup white vinegar, $\frac{1}{2}$ cup dish detergent, $\frac{1}{4}$ cup water with 2 teaspoons of mayonnaise (not low-cal).

SWEET GRIT

To remove garden stains from your hands, try placing about $\frac{1}{2}$ teaspoon of sugar with the soap lather when you wash your hands, you will be amazed how easy the stains are removed.

THE MAD SCIENTIST

The formula for good liquid hand soap is one 4oz bar of soap, preferably one that has a moisturizing cream, and 3 cups of water. Grate the soap as fine as possible then add the water. Microwave on high till dissolved stirring every few minutes; then allow it to cool before using.

A LITTLE SQUIRT

If you want your makeup to last longer, try spraying your face first with mineral water and allowing it to dry.

HOT AND COLD

If you break your lipstick, try heating the broken ends over a matchstick until they are soft; place them together and place in the freezer.

NO HANGING AROUND ANYMORE

If hangnails are bothersome, try rubbing vitamin E oil around the cuticles.

SHADES OF LAWRENCE WELK

To make your own bubble bath liquid, try placing soap slivers in a porous draw-string bag. Attach the bag to the tap while the water is filling the tub and instant bubble bath. Place herbs in the bag for a pleasant fragrance.

CARE FOR YOU'RE FACE

If you rub the inner part of an apple peel on your face, it will give you a complexion glow.

CHAPTER 14

EVERYDAY HOUSEHOLD PRODUCTS

HOW CAN I MAKE AN EFFECTIVE GROUT CLEANER?

Cleaning grout around tiles is one of the worst cleaning jobs in the home. Most common products contain sodium hypochlorite (similar to diluted laundry bleach) and/or calcium hypochlorite and some detergent. An inexpensive grout cleaner may be made by mixing together 2 parts of liquid laundry bleach with $1/2$ part of a phosphate-based liquid floor cleaner (or 2tbl of Spic & Span), 3 parts of isopropyl alcohol, and $4^{1}/_{2}$ parts of water. The solution can be placed in a clean plastic pump bottle and used the same as the store cleaners. When mixing chemicals be sure and do not place any near an open flame or heating element. The isopropyl alcohol is flammable.

SHOULD WE USE A PHOSPHATE DETERGENT?

Phosphates increase the alkalinity of wash water and are more effective than the older products that used washing soda. Phosphates tend to bind certain metal salts that are found in hard water and change them into soft water, which makes the fabric more accessible to the detergent. Sometimes phosphates are called sodium triployphosphate (STPP), which is an inexpensive form and harmless to humans.

WHAT OTHER CHEMICALS BESIDE SOAP ARE IN LAUNDRY DETERGENT?

There are a number of other chemicals in most laundry detergents, these include; bleaches, perfumes, enzymes, redeposition agents, surfacants, and even chemicals to prevent your washer from being damaged. Some products even use optical brighteners, which are dyes that are deposited on your garments that will transmit light to the human eye that would ordinarily be invisible; and ultraviolet light rays. When you see an advertising that claims its products will make your clothes "whiter than white" it is really not possible they only appear to be. One of the more interesting agents is the anti-redeposition agents that coat the clothes with a type of cotton-like substance (carboxymetacellulose) that can prevent the dirt and grime that has been washed from the garments to be re-deposited back on the clothes during the wash cycle. The agent is easily removed during the rinse cycle. The most difficult stains for a detergent to remove are the protein stains from dairy products, eggs, and blood.

WHAT DO FABRIC SOFTENERS ACTUALLY DO?

Fabric softeners are made from chemicals called "cationic surfacants" or resins. The cationic surfacants possess a positive charge and have an affinity for wet, negatively charged garments. They form an even layer on the surface of the garment removing the negative charge, which is responsible for a scratchy feeling and roughness of the fabric. The softener will also remove the static electricity from the fabric and generally makes the fabric softer to the touch.

WHAT CAUSES THE RINGS ON TOILET BOWLS?

The ring around the bowl is caused by the accumulation of dirt embedding in minerals from the hard water. Minerals that are usually found in these residues are either calcium or magnesium carbonate. A mild acid will easily remove the stains, the most common and least expensive is oxalic acid which is available in a powder or flake form. A cola drink that contains phosphoric acid and has gone flat will also do the job in some instances.

WHAT IS SOAP MADE OUT OF?

Whether you use soft soap or hard soap they are all made from sodium or ammonium hydroxide and one of the following: An animal fat product, usually tallow, coconut oil (lauric acid), oleic acid (olive oil), cottonseed oil (linoleic acid), or isethionic acid. Soaps may contain perfumes, skin conditioners, or antibacterial agents. Most are non-irritating to the skin and lather well and have good cleansing ability.

HOW IS TALLOW PRODUCED?

Tallow is a substance that is derived by passing steam through animal fat. The lighter fat is stearic acid and the sodium salt of stearic acid is called sodium sterate, which is found in bar soap as sodium tallowate. Coconut oil: because of its liquid form and is more unsaturated than tallow make it a better choice for a soap product.

WHY DOES IVORY SOAP FLOAT?

Excess air is mixed in with the ingredients, which allows it to float. The floating soap was produced by accident when in 1930 an employee who was supposed to be watching the soap mixture fell asleep and the mixture accidentally filled with air. The company didn't want to discard the batch and found that the public liked the floating soap.

IS COLD CREAM THE SAME AS CLEANSING CREAM?

Cleansing creams or cold creams are basically the same product. They are composed of camphor, clove oil, menthol, phenol, linseed oil, water, stearic acid, soybean oil, eucalyptus oil, calcium hydroxide, and aluminum hydroxide. Camphor, clove oil, and eucalyptus oil are aromatics. The menthol has some antibacterial properties as well as being an astringent, soybean oil adds a smooth texture, stearic acid prepares the skin so that the cream will penetrate, linseed oil is a softening agent, phenol is a relatively strong antibacterial agent, and a hydroxide will increase the pH.

ARE SHAMPOOS SIMILAR TO LIQUID DISH SOAP?

There are really no similarities between liquid dish soap and shampoo. Shampoos are produced from ammonium lauryl sulfonate and are much safer for your hair. Shampoos contain lauramide, which is used to produce lather, lecithin to give your hair a shine, hydrolyzed animal protein to repair those split ends. They also include glycol stearate to untangle your hair and give it luster, methylparaben to preserve the mixture and methylisothiozoline as an antibacterial agent, Canadian balsam as a lacquer, and some citric acid to make the mixture a bit more acidic with a lower pH. When shampoos are produced they end up too basic (alkaline) to be used on hair and must have the pH lowered.

HOW DOES HAIR SPRAY WORK

When you spray hair spray, you are depositing a thin layer of resin, which is dissolved in a volatile solvent or alcohol, which easily evaporates in the air. Once the solvent evaporates it leaves behind a layer of "plastic." Hair sprays in standard pump applicators (non-aerosal type) are really "plasticizers." If you don't believe that there is a thin layer of plastic on your hair, just take a flat glass surface and spray a thick layer on the glass. Allow it to dry for a minute or so then just peel off the layer in one thin sheet. Mousses, gels, and creams for the hair are also a type of plasticizer.

HOW DOES A LIQUID HAIR REMOVER WORK?

A hair remover is called a "depilatory." These products remove body hair using a concentrated chemical solution to break the sulfide bonds in hair. The main chemical used is calcium thioglycolate and in high concentrations is capable of breaking down almost 100% of the disulfide bonds in hair, thus causing the hair to literally fall apart and disintegrate. The minute fragments of hair are then removed with washing.

WHAT IS TOOTHPASTE COMPOSED OF?

There are a number of chemicals that all work together to grind off stains, help prevent cavities, wash away the debris, and a flavoring. The abrasives to remove stains may include any of the following: hydrated silica, calcium carbonate, baking soda, calcium pyrophosphate, hydrated aluminum oxide, magnesium carbonate, or tricalcium phosphate. The moisturizing agent is usually sorbitol; the chemical that prevents the conversion of plaque to tartar is tetrapotassium pyrophosphate; the sweetener may be sodium saccharin; one of the more popular whiteners is titanium dioxide; a thickening agent is needed which is carbomer; and of course of number of artificial dyes F,D, and C blue #1. Using baking soda after each meal may be just as effective as this chemical smorgasbord.

HOW DO ANTIPERSPIRANTS AND DEODORANTS DIFFER?

The first antiperspirant was produced about 1905 and was called "Odo-Ro-No." Early deodorants were actually just underarm perfumes. Antiperspirants are formulated to cause the sweat glands to constrict and actually prevent normal perspiration. Since bacteria need a certain amount of moisture to reproduce, the sweat provides a perfect medium for them to live and produce offensive odors. Antiperspirants contain chemicals that prevent the problem from occurring these include aluminum chlorohydrate, aluminum chloride, or zirconium chloride. Sticks are more effective due to their solid composition. Creams and sprays tend to lose effectiveness too soon.

Deodorants do not act to constrict the sweat glands but they do contain antibacterial agents, the most effective being triclosan. The antibacterial effects are only effective for about 2-3 hours and most deodorants contain a perfume to hide the offensive odors. Deodorants are used by people who would prefer a more natural approach and they would prefer not to have normal bodily process altered.

WHY ARE AFTERSHAVE LOTIONS USED?

Aftershave lotions tend to cool the skin, tighten the pores, and promote healing from the irritation of shaving. The most common ingredients used to accomplish these tasks are propylene glycol, menthol, and benzoic acid. Pre-shave lotions are only used with electric shavers and are skin lubricants that help the shaver glide more easily across the skin. Some have ingredients that may also make the facial hair stand up to be cut.

WHAT IS VASELINE MADE OUT OF?

Vaseline is produced from a mixture of hydrocarbons that are derived from purified crude oil. Petroleum jelly is excellent for sealing off the skin and protecting it from surface damage, especially from irritations and a mild abrasion.

WHAT IS THE DIFFERENCE IN OVER-THE-COUNTER PAIN RELIEVERS?

The most common analgesics (pain relievers) are aspirin, acetaminophen, ibuprofen, and naproxen. Aspirin has the capability of reducing inflammation in joints and act as an antipyretic (fever reducer). Ibuprofen is supposed to be more effective for deep muscle pain; however, it has yet to be clinically proven to the satisfaction of the medical community. Naproxen is similar in action to ibuprofen but tends to remain in the bloodstream for about 2-3 hours longer, which may provide a plus.

Acetaminophen AKA Paracetamol in England does not seem to offer any relief for inflammation and not as good a pain reliever as aspirin but does not irritate the stomach, which aspirin may do. A relative newcomer is naproxen sodium sold under the brand name of Aleve. Naproxen sodium may irritate the stomach just as much as aspirin and is sold to relieve pain, backache, muscle pain, discomfort of arthritis, and menstrual cramping.

Aspirin works by slowing the transmission of nerve impulses to the brain reducing the sensation of pain. It also interferes with prostaglandins, which when in excess, tend to dilate the small vessels in the brain causing headaches by localized inflammation.

STOMACH IRRITATION BY ASPIRIN IS USUALLY THE RESULT OF NOT DRINKING A FULL GLASS OF WATER WHEN TAKING THE PRODUCT.

WHY ARE SO MANY HOSPITALS USING TYLENOL

Tylenol is selling the hospitals their product at below cost to promote their product as one of the more popular analgesics used by the medical community. Bayer is also trying this method and is making some inroads. Once the patient leaves the hospital most physicians advise their patients to purchase any over-the-counter pain reliever.

WHY DO LINIMENTS REDUCE PAIN?

Liniment has been used for hundreds of years on both animals and humans to relieve pain, especially pain related to muscle overuse. They are mainly in cream form, however, there are still a few that are in liquid form. The creams tend to stay on better and allow the chemicals to do their job more efficiently. Liniments work by a process called, counter-irritation. They actually irritate the skin to such a degree that they cause a mild pain, which causes the pain receptors in the area to be "switched off." A common liniment for horses, DMSO is not recommended for humans, DMSO tends to dilate surface blood vessels and will allow almost any medication or chemical to enter circulation.

WHY CAN'T I KEEP THAT NEW CAR SMELL LONGER?

A number of products have that same "new car" smell for a short period of time, especially new carpets. During the manufacture of plastics, oils are added to the plastic to keep it from drying out. These special oils are absorbed into the plastic and over a short period of time their vapors come into the air. The oils that are left on the surface are the ones you smell when you purchase a new item then over a period of time, the deeper internal oils come to the surface but are not strong enough to create a noticeable odor.

ARE OVEN CLEANERS DANGEROUS?

The majority of aerosol oven cleaners contain sodium hydroxide (lye) which is also found in drain cleaners. When lye is sprayed on burnt fats and carbohydrates it converts them into soap that is easily wiped off with a damp cloth. It would be best to use a number of the newer products that use organic salts and are less dangerous, however, with any type of oven cleaner make sure that there is good ventilation or they may burn the lining of your mouth and throat.

HOW DOES ANTIFREEZE WORK

Antifreeze is composed mainly of propylene alcohol which when added to water lowers the freezing point and also increases the boiling point. Therefore water can't freeze at 32° F. and it will not boil at 212°F. The coolant is circulated through the engine by the water pump and the engine heat is transferred to the coolant, which returns to the radiator. The radiator is cooled by the outside air, which cools the antifreeze preventing boil-over.

CAN COLA REALLY CLEAN MY CAR BATTERY?

Carbonated beverages especially those that are carbonated using phosphoric acid will dissolve metal oxides that cake on battery terminals. However, the best way to clean the terminals is with a metal brush and some baking soda sprinkled on first to neutralize the acid. Never clean the battery terminals with water, the battery may short out and explode.

WHY DON'T CARS WANT TO START ON COLD DAYS?

The problem usually has nothing to do with the battery but with the oil. Freezing temperature tend to turn your oil into a thick syrup making your battery work harder to turn the engine over. Manufacturers make higher amp batteries that may help alleviate this problem or you may want to consider a heated blanket to keep the motor oil from becoming a semi-solid.

WHAT IS THE DIFFERENCE BETWEEN A CAR POLISH AND A WAX?

A car polish is only meant to enhance and restore the luster to a wax coating. They remove dirt and debris trapped in the wax and restore, a smooth finish to the surface. The polish will not provide any protection, it will just keep the wax clean.

WHAT IS THE DIFFERENCE BETWEEN CEMENT AND CONCRETE?

Cement is mainly composed of limestone (calcium carbonate), calcium oxide, clay, and usually shale. The ingredients absorb water, which turns it into a paste. Concrete is cement with the addition of sand, gravel, and crushed rock. The addition of these ingredients lowers the cost since pure cement is very expensive. The hardening process of cement is somewhat complicated, however, the moistened mixture containing calcium, aluminum, and silicon salts tend to interact and produce a new substance called tricalcium aluminates. These are inorganic compounds that after a few days form, interlocking crystals that produces the concrete's strength.

WHAT IS STAINLESS STEEL MADE OF?

When stainless steel is produced, iron and chromium are mixed together with the percentage of chromium at about 12%. As long as the alloy contains the 12% a percentage of the chromium will rise to the surface of the metal and will form a thin coating of chromium oxide, which protects the iron from rusting and gives it a shiny surface. Other metals are sometimes added such as nickel to increase the strength of the stainless steel.

EVERYDAY HOUSEHOLD PRODUCTS — 111

WHAT MAKES A DISINFECTANT DIFFERENT FROM AN ANTISEPTIC?

Antiseptics are chemical agents that kill a percentage of bacteria, however, they don't kill all bacteria but they are effective in preventing the growth of most bacteria. Antiseptics are mainly used on a cut or abrasion. Disinfectants are formulated to kill all bacteria and viruses but are too harsh to be applied to your skin.

KEEP YOUR FIZZLE IN

The refrigerator is a good place to store many chemicals such as hydrogen peroxide. It will stay active for a longer period of time. Nail polish is another chemical that likes the cold and will go on smoother.

HOW DOES INSTANT HOT SHAVING CREAMS WORK?

A number of shaving creams advertise that they heat up on your face to provide a more comfortable shaving experience. These products use compounds such as methyl salicitate or salicylic acid to actually irritate the skin causing a sensation of heat by increasing the circulation of blood in that area where it is applied. The same ingredients can be found in a number of liniments.

WHAT HAPPENS WHEN YOU HAVE YOUR HAIR STRAIGHTENED?

Hairs are linked together by a chemical bond called a "disulfide bond." These sulfur atoms are attracted to each other and form a bond, which can be broken using a chemical called thioglycolic acid. When this is applied the bonds release and become free allowing the hair to relax.

DO I NEED A SPECIAL DETERGENT FOR COLD WATER WASHING?

It is not necessary to purchase a special cold water detergent. The differences in hot and cold water detergents is so insignificant that it a waste of money if there is a difference in cost. There is only one compound that is capable of changing the effectiveness of any detergent when it is used in cold water and that is the amount of surfacant they use and almost all are at the same level. A surfacant will actually make the water "wetter" by changing the surface tension allowing the water and detergent: to more freely enter the garment.

DO DRY BLEACHES WORK BETTER THAN LIQUID BLEACHES?

There is a misconception that bleaches remove stains. Bleaches do not remove stains, they only mask the stain so that you will not see it. This process is known as oxidation and utilizes one of two types of bleach. The dry bleach is composed of sodium perborate, which is converted to hydrogen peroxide, which continues to break down liberating oxygen gas, which then oxidizes the clothing. Liquid bleach contains the chemical sodium hypochlorite which cause the release of chlorine gas that oxidizes the clothing, thus bleaching the stain out. The more powerful of the two bleaching agents is the liquid bleach.

NATURAL REMEDIES & NUTRITION

WHAT IS THE SECRET FORMULA OF THOSE MAGICAL SPOT REMOVERS?

The TV commercials and newspaper ads announcing that there is a cleaner that will take any spot or stain out of any fabric is just a combination of a detergent and bleach combined. Most of these are sold through good advertising and sales techniques. Most do work well, however, you could probably make them with two or three ingredients you already have at home.

WHAT IS THE DIFFERENCE BETWEEN SYNTHETIC AND NATURAL FIBERS?

Synthetic or permanent press fabrics are produced from either 100% synthetic or natural fibers that contain sufficient quantities of plastic added to give the desired qualities the manufacturer requires. Permanent press fabrics will retain their shape up to the point that they will start to melt, which is a very high temperature and never achieved when they are washed or dry cleaned. Because of the plastic used in the synthetics, the fabric is very dense and will not lose their shape. Natural fiber garments are not very dense therefore they are unable to retain their shape very well, especially creases.

ARE THE EXPENSIVE BATHTUB CLEANERS REALLY NECESSARY?

Most bathtub cleaners advertise that they contain powerful disinfectants that will kill bacteria as well as cleaning off the soap scum and dirt residues. While they do contain disinfectants, the bacteria killing action only lasts for about 3-4 hours and then the bacteria come right back. The best cleaner for tubs is diluted laundry bleach. If you can't handle the smell, purchase one that is scented. Be sure and wear gloves and ventilate the room well when using bleach of any type.

WHAT DO THOSE LARGE TOILET CLEANING TABLETS REALLY DO?

The bowl-cleaning tablets that are placed into the toilet tank are not going to clean your toilet, they are only designed to slow down the process of hard-water buildup, which contains imbedded dirt and debris. They contain a strong chlorine bleach compound or quaternary ammonium chloride. Both are strong disinfectants and have good cleaning properties. Some products, however, may be so strong that they will cause scaling of any metal surface in the tank and may cause the toilet to clog up.

DO THE COLORED RIBBONS OF TOOTHPASTE CONTAIN DIFFERENT INGREDIENTS?

Toothpaste that comes out of the tube in different colors is all the same product, just dyed red and green. Recently, a new product did come on the market with a plunger and two compartments in the container that provides you with two different ingredients to care for your teeth and gums. Check with your dentist before using the product since it contains hydrogen peroxide.

WHAT'S IN A BREATH MINT AND HOW DOES IT WORK?

Breath mints contain sweeteners, moisturizers, and may contain a germ killer. Most brands contain sorbitol as the sweetener, which may cause diarrhea if too much is consumed in susceptible individuals. The odor eaters are probably chlorophyll and "Retsyn" which is another name for cuprous (copper) gluconate.

WHAT, IS THE DIFFERENCE IN PERFUME, COLOGNE, AND TOILET WATER?

The main difference is the concentration of the compounds used that are responsible for the aroma of each product. Perfumes are produced with the highest concentrations and therefore last longer. If you place a small amount of Vaseline on the areas you are applying the perfume to it will last twice as long. Colognes contain less of the same compound and more fillers while toilet water is just diluted cologne. The cost of most perfumes is determined by the amount of money that is spent in advertising and in-store marketing of the product.

WHAT MAKES TOILET TISSUES DIFFERENT

The better brands and of course, the more expensive ones are made from purified wood pulp and skin softeners. The other products are only made from purified wood pulp and they do not go through any softening process and you should have no problem telling the difference. Colored toilet paper contains traces of metals that produce the different colors. Occasionally people with very sensitive skin may experience a reaction from the colored papers.

DO ACNE MEDICATIONS WORK?

Acne medications do not cure acne they only provide a measure of control. Studies show that diet doesn't have much of an effect either. Keeping the face clean with soap and water seems to work almost as well as some of the medications. The preparations contain a chemical sponge, which may contain sulfur and salicylic creams as the absorbent to possibly soak up the excess skin oils. The oils are actually more related to pimples than acne. One of the more common methods is to soak a cotton ball in alcohol and use that to cleanse the area.

HOW DO PREPARATIONS THAT CLAIM TO COAT THE STOMACH ACTUALLY WORK?

These preparations absorb large quantities of water and waste food materials in the stomach and upper small intestine. By doing this it allows the areas to "dry out" and protects the delicate stomach lining against any additional infection. These coating products contain purified clay, aluminum magnesium silicate, bismuth salts, and usually activated charcoal.

DOES COLA REALLY CONTROL NAUSEA AND VOMITING?

Nausea and vomiting can be controlled by medications called "antiemetics." These antiemetics, of which Emetrol is one of the most popular ones, control the "gag reflex" and are very effective. However, Coca-Cola syrup or almost any other cola syrup which contain sugar and phosphates are every bit as effective in most instances. Your pharmacist may be able to assist you in obtaining cola syrup. Diet colas will not work since they do not contain sugar.

HOW DOES BAKING SODA REMOVE ODORS?

Sodium bicarbonate (baking soda) is an inorganic powder, which simply means that it is not produced from living matter and is sold in very fine particles with a high surface area. House odors are composed of organic oils that become stuck in the powder and neutralized as if taken into a sponge. When the oils remain in the soda they eventually become inactivated permanently.

HOW DOES ELECTRIC AIR CLEANERS WORK?

The newer electric air cleaners draw the air over a series of electrically charged metal plates that attract dust and pollutants. The plates must be removed periodically and cleaned. Another type is the porous silicon plate, which traps the particles like a magnet. This type of unit utilizes a blower motor to pass the air over the filters, which need to be washed.

DO WINDSHIELD DEICERS REALLY WORK?

Most windshield deicers are made from alcohol and are overpriced products. They do, however, work fairly well depending on the thickness of the ice. If the ice is very thick it will take quite a while for the ice to melt. Never place hot water on your windshield; it may cause the glass to expand from the heat and then contract when it cools, cracking the windshield. Most deicers are similar to antifreeze. You can place a solution of homemade deicer in your window washer unit; just mix 1 part of any commercial antifreeze with 9 parts of 50/50 mixture of alcohol and water.

WHAT IS A PAINT PRIMER?

These are usually colorless and will cause paint to adhere to surfaces better. Colored primers hide a color that may bleed through. Primers may also be used to protect a metal surface from corrosion as an undercoat. Since many paints do not adhere well to a number of surfaces, primers are a necessity in many instances.

WHAT CAN I USE TO CLEAN SILVERSTONE AND TEFLON POTS?

For the most part these plastic coated pots are easy to keep clean, however, they do stain and may over time develop a buildup of grease and oil. If this occurs it will adversely affect the efficiency of the non-stick surface. To clean the surface, just mix 2 tablespoons of baking soda with $1/2$ cup of white vinegar in 1 cup of water and clean the pot by placing the ingredients into the pot, place the pot on the range and boil it for about 10 minutes. Wash the pot, then rub vegetable oil on the surface of the plastic coating to re-season it.

HOW CAN I UNCLOG A DRAIN USING INGREDIENTS AROUND THE KITCHEN

After trying "plumbers helper" with no success, try the following method. Remove all standing water so that you are able to pour the ingredients into the drain. First pour 1 cup of baking soda, 1 cup of table salt, and $\frac{1}{2}$ cup of white vinegar into the clogged drain. These will start dissolving any organic matter and grease away immediately. Allow to stand for 5 minutes then flush 1-2 quarts of boiling water down the drain.

HOW DO YOU CLEAN A THERMOS BOTTLE?

The easiest way to eliminate the odors and stains is to fill the container with hot water and drop in a denture cleaning tablet, then allow it to stand overnight. Baking soda will also work, but not as well.

HOW DO YOU MAKE A CANDLE ALMOST DRIP-LESS?

Prepare a solution of 2 tablespoons of salt per candle in just enough water to cover the candles. Allow the candles to soak in the saltwater solution for about 2-3 hours, then rinse them, let them dry, and wait at least 24 hours before you use them. The saltwater hardens the wax and allows the wax more time to burn cleaner reducing the chance of dripping on the tablecloth.

ALL CHOPSTICKS ARE NOT THE SAME

If you have ever eaten in a Japanese restaurant you will notice that the chopsticks are pointed. In a Chinese restaurant the chopsticks are blunt. Many restaurants will Americanize the chopsticks by placing a rubber, band around them about $\frac{1}{4}$ of the way down from the top. This will hold them together and make them easier to handle.

WHAT IS AN EASY METHOD OF OVEN CLEANING

If you have an oven that is not equipped with a self-cleaning feature then just pre-heat the oven to 200ºF and turn it off. Place a small bowl with $\frac{1}{2}$ cup of ammonia on the center shelf then close the oven and allow it to stand overnight. The next day, open the oven and allow it to air for 30 minutes in a well, ventilated kitchen then wipe up the mess with a warm, damp paper towel.

THE AVERAGE LIFESPAN OF HOUSEHOLD APPLIANCES

CLOTHES DRYER . . . . .18 YEARS
WASHING MACHINE . . . . .14 YEARS
CENTRAL AIR CONDITIONER/HEAT PUMP . . . .17 YEARS
WINDOW AIR CONDITIONER . . . . .12 YEARS
REFRIGERATOR . . . . .20 YEARS
DISHWASHER . . . . .12 YEARS
UPRIGHT FREEZER . . . . .20 YEARS
KITCHEN RANGE . . . . .18 YEARS
KITCHEN OVEN . . . . .17 YEARS
WATER HEATER . . . . .12 YEARS

CHAPTER 15

HOME AND GARDEN TIPS

HOME

MODERATION, A MUST

If you are going to paint cabinet doors, try rubbing a small amount of Vaseline on the hinges, it will make removing the paint easier.

THE HOLY HOSE

When your garden hose has a leak, don't throw it out, just add more holes and make a sprinkler.

GOING ON VACATION?

Best to unplug the garage door. Thieves go through neighborhoods and check factory codes. Best to put in a new code when purchasing a garage door or buying a home.

SQUECKY FLOORS?

Try placing talcum powder in the cracks between boards.

ELIMINATE PAINT SMELLS

Stir 1 tablespoon of vanilla into every gallon of paint. Will not affect the paint.

PAINT DROPS KEEP FALLING ON YOUR HEAD....

If you are going to paint a ceiling, try cutting a tennis ball in half and placing a half on the brush to catch the drips.

THE DISAPPEARING ACT

If you are sure you will use up all the paint in a can, try punching a few holes near the rim you are removing the paint from. The paint that is wiped off the brush will go back into the can.

NOT A SHOCKING EXPERIENCE

To remove a broken light bulb, turn off the electricity; then try placing $\frac{1}{2}$ a raw potato or $\frac{1}{2}$ a small apple into the broken base and screwing out.

ELIMINATING WRINKLES FROM VINYL COATS

Use a hair dryer on the wrinkles while the coat is hanging up.

CALL SMOKY

If you have a charcoal filter in your range-hood, it can be recharged by placing it in a 450° F oven for 30 minutes after completely cleaning the frame. If there is any grease left on the frame it may catch on fire or smoke up the house.

DUNK IT, DIP IT

When painting anything, make sure you dip a 3 X 5 index card into the paint to make it easier to match it at a later date if needed.

GOING DOWN

Old nuts and bolts make excellent sinkers when you are going fishing.

STATIC ELECTRICITY

If a pin or needle will not penetrate an article, try rubbing it in your hair before trying it again.

I CAN SEE A RAINBOW

If you want to add color to a campfire, try soaking pinecones in a solution of $\frac{1}{2}$ gallon of water and $\frac{1}{2}$ pound of Borax.

REAL SHARPIE

An easy way to sharpen scissors is to fold a piece of aluminum foil 3-4 times, then cut through it several times.

RETURNING TO LIFE

Those dented up ping pong balls can be revived by placing them into very hot water for about 20 minutes. The air in the ball will expand enough to pop out the dents.

DON'T GET ZAPPED

Microwave doors may become misaligned, especially if you tend to lean on them occasionally. They will leak radiation and should be checked periodically with a small inexpensive detector that can be purchased in any hardware store.

FILLER UP

If you need to repair a hole in a piece of wood, try adding a small amount of instant coffee to the spackling or a thick paste made from a laundry starch and warm water.

BUY A NEW LID

If you lose a top knob to a saucepan lid, try placing a screw with the thread side up into the hole then attaching a cork on it.

SNOW SLIDE

If you want the snow to slide off your snow shovel with ease, all you have to do is save your empty butter wrappers and wipe the shovel off before using it.

SEEING THE LIGHT

Mirrors can be brightened by rubbing them with a cloth dampened with alcohol. Alcohol will remove a thin film of oil that is left from cleaning agents.

HOW TO DETECT A TWO-WAY MIRROR

Place the tip of your finger against the glass, if you see a gap between your finger and the image of your finger it is a real mirror. If there is no gap it is a two-way mirror.

GETTING A NEW LEASE ON LIFE

If your flashlight batteries are becoming weak while on a camping trip, try placing them in the sunlight for 6-8 hours; this should give them back some additional life.

DOING THE TWIST

Hair dryer cords can be kept neat using ponytail holders.

SPRINKLE, SPRINKLE, LITTLE SALT

Place salt on fireplace logs to reduce the soot in the house.

A SWEETER YULE

To preserve your Christmas tree for a few extra days, try adding a small amount of sugar or Pinesol™ to the water.

SMOOTHIE

When applying wallpaper, try using a paint roller instead of a sponge to smooth the paper out.

HOP, SCOTCH

If you need to paint steps, try painting every other step, when those are dry go back and paint the rest. This will allow you continued access to the upstairs.

COLA WORKS GREAT TOO

If you're having a problem with a rusty nut or bolt, try placing a few drops of ammonia or hydrogen peroxide on it for 30 minutes.

FILLER UP

If you have a small hole in a window screen, try using a number of layers of clear nail polish.

MR. CLEAN

If you place masking tape on the rim of paint can before pouring the paint out, you can remove the tape later and the rim will be clean.

LUMPLESS PAINT

If you have lumps in your paint can, try cutting a piece of screen the size of the can and allowing it to settle to the bottom, it will carry the lumps to the bottom.

FOUR EYES

When painting ceilings, try wearing a pair of old plastic goggles.

PAM TO THE RESCUE

Squeaky door and cabinet hinges as well as sticky locks can be sprayed with a non-stick vegetable spray.

SAFETY FIRST

If you need to get a closer look at your roof or second story, try using a pair of binoculars instead of a ladder.

FINDING A REAL STUD

If you don't have a stud finder, try using a compass, holding it level with the floor and at a right angle to the wall. Then slowly move the compass along the surface of the wall, when the needle moves that's where you will find a stud.

HOW TO GET A RUN IN YOUR PANTYHOSE

Whenever you are using sandpaper to finish a wood surface, try placing an old nylon stocking over your hand and running it over the surface, the slightest rough spot will be found.

PEEK-A-BOO

To avoid getting locked out of your house, try placing an extra key in a plastic baggie and placing it under a rock in the garden or bury it behind a plant or tree.

DRIP, DRIP, DRIP

If you're worried about your water lines freezing just leave one of the taps running very slightly to avoid the problem. If you have a two-story house, open one on the first floor.

DON'T PAINT YOUR PORES

Using a hand moisturizer when painting or doing other dirty chores will prevent dirt and paint from seeping into you're skin pores, making personal cleanup easier.

HANDY RULER

Remember a dollar bill is 6 inches long and almost 3-inches wide.

VASE OR THERMOS STAINS

If you have a stain on the bottom of a vase or in a thermos, just fill the vessel with water and drop in 2 Alka-Seltzer® tablets in and allow to stand overnight.

BUBBLE, BUBBLE, TOIL AND TROUBLE

Varnish never needs stirring. Stirring only creates air bubbles, which may ruin a smooth finish.

ODE DE CEDAR CHEST

If you would like the original cedar odor from an old cedar chest, try rubbing the inner surface lightly with fine sandpaper.

ALL-PURPOSE, OF COURSE

If you are painting old woodwork that has small holes that need patching, try filling the holes with flour and some of the paint, it will harden and will not be noticeable.

ARE YOUR DRAWERS A PROBLEM

If you are having problems with sticky drawers, try rubbing a candle along the tops of the runners.

PATIO FURNITURE TIPS

Aluminum furniture: apply a layer of paste wax to avoid pitting. Wicker furniture: clean with a mild solution of salt water and it won't yellow. Wrought iron: paint with aluminum paint, then apply a layer of paste wax.

PLOP, PLOP

To clean a toilet, just drop in 2 Alka-Seltzer® tablets in and wait 20 minutes. Brush and flush and stains begone.

A CHILLING SOLUTION

If you don't feel like cleaning a roller, place it in a plastic bag and place in the freezer. This will keep it moist and usable for a few days.

AND A LONNNNG EXTENSION CORD

If your pipes freeze and do not burst, try using a hair dryer to defrost them.

TRY TO KEEP IT TOGETHER

Lightweight materials that need to be glued together are easily held in place with spring clothespins.

SOFTENING THEM UP

When your paint brushes harden, try softening them by soaking them in full strength white vinegar them cleaning with a comb.

PAINT HOLDERS

Empty nail polish bottles make excellent holders for touch-up paints.

KEEPING GREASE IN ITS PLACE

If you have grease spots after removing old wallpaper, try applying a coat of clear varnish to the spots. The grease won't soak through to the new paper.

BALLOONING

If you are going to store a partially used can of paint, try placing a blown-up balloon the size of the space in the can. It will reduce the air in the can and keep the paint fresher longer.

SUN-DRYING YOUR BOTTOM

If you have a cane-bottomed chair that has loosened, try applying very hot water to the underside and allowing the chair to stand in direct sunlight until it dries.

A WASTE OF A COOL ONE

If you wish to "frost" a bathroom window, use a solution of 1 cup of "Lite" beer mixed in 4 tablespoons of Epsom salts. Paint the mixture on the window, it will wash off easily.

HOW DRY I AM

Bathroom fixtures should be painted with special epoxy paint because of exposure to moisture.

A SHINING EXAMPLE

Enamel or oil paint can easily be removed from your hands with paste floor wax then washing with soap and water.

SKIN TIP

To prevent a skin forming on top of the paint, try placing a piece of waxed paper the size of the opening on top of the paint.

OIL YOUR BRISTLES

After you clean out a paintbrush, rub a few drops of vegetable oil into the bristles to keep them soft.

I WONDER WHERE THE YELLOW WENT....

If you add 7-10 drops of black paint to each quart of white paint, it will not yellow.

TILL YOUR OLD AND GRAY

If you "weather" wood before applying stain, the stain will last years longer.

MAY HAVE A NEGATIVE EFFECT

If you run out of salt or sand to de-ice your walkway, try using kitty litter. Keep the cat in the house!

FOR SAFETY'S SAKE

If you want to fireproof your Christmas tree, try spraying a mixture of 8 ounces boric acid in one gallon of water on the tree then allow it to dry.

BE FIRM WITH YOUR GUTTERS

If you need to clean your gutters, try using an old fan belt. It has excellent flexibility, and is firm enough to do the job without scrapping the paint off.

HOLES IN YOUR PANTYHOE

Use a small amount of clear nail polish on a small hole and it will stop the area from running any further.

DON'T TREAD ON THEM

Linoleum or floor tiles are excellent for covering the tops of picnic tables. A piece of linoleum can also be used instead of contact paper on kitchen shelves. It will last longer and is easier to keep clean.

ELECTRICIANS TRICK

Electrical cords should be stored in cardboard tubes from rolls of paper towels. Then label them as to which appliance they go to.

GETTING ON THE RIGHT TRACK

Windows will slide more easily if you rub a bar of soap across the track occasionally.

RUST PREVENTION

If you place a few mothballs, a piece of chalk, or a piece of charcoal in your tool-box you will never have any rust on the tools.

STOP SMOKING

To reduce fireplace smoking, try placing a brick under each leg of the grate.

OUCH

Use a split piece of old garden hose to cover the blades of a saw when storing it to be safe.

CLAY IS POROUS

Never place a clay pot on wooden furniture, water seeps through and can damage the wood.

GOING DOWN?

If you need to use a ladder on soft earth, try placing a coffee can under each leg.

BIG BAGGIE

If you need to store furniture or chairs outdoors, place a large plastic bag over them.

GARDEN

NATURAL FERTILIZERS

A number of foods make excellent fertilizers. Banana skins and eggshells are on top of the list. The minerals provided are for the most part not found in many fertilizers. Flat club soda also makes an excellent fertilizer. A sip or two occasionally will perk up their colors.

DON'T THROW OUT THE EMPTY MILK CARTON OR BEER CANS

After you use up all the milk, just place some water in the container, swish it around a little and water your plants. This will give the plants a growth booster. Beer works just as well and helps the plants grow stronger and taller from the yeast.

ROSES LIKE FAT DRIPPINGS

Place a small amount of old fat drippings at the base of a rose bush and it will be healthier and bloom more frequently.

THE GREEN, GREEN GRASS

If your grass is not as green as you would like, it may be deficient in magnesium and iron.

JACK FROST IS NO PROBLEM

If you think that a frost is coming and you need to protect your plants, just spray them with a light coat of cold water in the evening. The water will generate enough heat while it is evaporating to prevent damage from the frost.

GLUB, GLUB

When cutting flowers from your garden, be sure and cut them only in the late evening or early morning. Have a bucket of water with you and use very sharp shears. After you cut the flowers, place the stem under water and cut the stem again on the diagonal, the stem, will them take in water and not, air.

LONG-LASTING ROSES

Just a capful of hydrogen peroxide in the vase every time you change the water will extend the life of roses.

GREAT EGG-WATER FERTILIZER

Never throw away the water after you boil eggs, just feed your plants with this high mineral fertilizer.

WEED-A-WAY

To remove unwanted grass from between sidewalk and driveway cracks, try using vinegar and salt. Place the solution in a spray bottle and squirt.

LEFTOVER TEA TO THE RESCUE

Cold leftover tea contains tannins, which is a good plant food.

HOW DRY I AM

When transplanting, always use pre-moistened soil and peat moss to help retain the moisture.

A CLEAN LEAF IS A HAPPY LEAF

If you want your plant's leaves to shine, try placing a small amount of glycerin and water on them. Mix 1 tablespoon of glycerin to 1 quart of water. Another method is to just dip a cotton ball in milk or mineral oil and clean the leaves.

HAPPY SEEDS

$1/2$-gallon milk carton cut in half make an excellent seed starter flat.

PLANT SAVER

If you are going a long vacation and are unable to find someone to care for your plants, try placing a large container of water near your plants, place pieces of yarn in the water and then lay the ends across the stalks of the plants. Capillary action will keep the plants in good shape until you return.

GETTING POTTED

If you are going to re-pot a plant, try placing a small coffee filter on the bottom of the pot to eliminate the soil from leaking out.

ROCKY $1/2$

Be sure and place a $1/2$-inch layer of gravel on the top of the soil in window boxes to prevent splattering when they are watered.

DON'T THROW OUT THE EGGSHELLS

When starting seedlings, best to plant the seeds in egg shell halves. Crack the shells completely when you plant them to provide an excellent fertilizer.

ESPECIALLY HARD ROCK ONES

Broken cassette tapes make excellent ties for plants.

HEAD FOR THE SWAP MEET

Old ice cube trays make excellent herb starters.

GETTING A LEG UP

Nylon stocking or pantyhose make excellent storage holders for storing bulbs during the winter. Air is able to circulate avoiding a problem with mold. Store in a cool dry location.

KEEP INSECTS AWAY FROM PLANTS

Crush 1 bulb of garlic, 1 small onion and 1 Tbsp of cayenne pepper. Place the mixture in a blender and add 1 quart of water, blend well and allow it to stand for one hour. Add 1-Tbsp of Ivory Liquid soap and mix well before placing the mixture in a spray bottle and lightly misting the plant leaves.

THE LIVING CUP

Styrofoam cups make excellent plant starters and are easy to break apart when you decide to plant the plant in the garden.

IT WON'T MAKE THE ICE GROW

A lawn seeder or fertilizer spreader make an ideal unit for scattering sand or salt on ice.

DON'T CRACK-UP

To prevent plaster walls from cracking when driving a nail in for a picture hanger, try placing a small piece of tape over the spot before hammering in the nail.

BLACK FLIES BEGONE

Those little black flies will never bother your plants or you again if you just water your plant with a mixture of 2 tablespoons of ammonia, to each quart of water. It will also provide your plant with additional nitrogen.

HERE BUGGY, BUGGY, BUGGY

There are a number of plants that you should plant in your garden, since they tend to attract beneficial insects. These include sweet alyssum, meadow foam, dill, catmint, coriander, white yarrow, corn poppy and single-flowered sunflower.

PLANTS PROTECTING OTHER PLANTS

PLANT	PROTECTS	ADVANTAGE
Basil	Tomato Plants	Repels mosquitoes & flies
Dill	Cherry tomato plants	Stops the tomato hornworm
Garlic	Raspberries	Keeps Japanese beetles away
Lamb's Quarter	Corn	Traps aphids
African Marigold	All plants	Deters many varieties of bugs
Mint	Cabbage	Reduces number of white cabbage bugs
Nastrium	Fruit trees, radish	Deters a number of beetles, Bugs and aphids

EDIBLE PETALS AND BLOSSOMS, SPRUCE UP A DISH OR SALAD

There are many edible petals and blossoms. These include some that we are very familiar with such as squash blossoms, dandelion, chive blossoms, radish, strawberry, and pumpkin blossoms. The list also includes some that we may not be so familiar with but are just as edible such as borage, pansy, nasturtium, mustard flower, oregano, and lilac. The best parts to eat are the petals and blossoms except for the inner part of the blossom, which contain the male and female parts.

To be safe, it would be best not to eat any flower part if fertilizer or insecticide has been used on them or any other flower part from a florist since most of these have been sprayed with chemicals.

KEEP BACK, HORN WORMS

If you plant dill around your tomato plants, you will never have a problem with pesky tomato, horn worms.

CHAPTER 16

GETTING FIT AND STAYING FIT

METABOLISM, WHAT IS IT?

Metabolism is the process by which the body releases energy derived from nutrients. It is the sum of all chemical reactions of the body's cells. The cells produce the energy in the form of heat, or in muscle cells in the form of mechanical work.

The basic fuels are proteins, carbohydrates, and fats, which are converted into glucose by the liver, then travel to the cells for chemical processing by way of the Krebs cycle (complex biochemical pathway) and turned into usable energy.

Metabolic rates vary from individual to individual dependent on a person's age, sex, body size, activity level or thyroid activity. Metabolism is first in line when the body distributes the energy it produces, the body must have energy to run the heart, and vital organs before anything else. Physical activity energy is only available after the more important needs are met.

A common question asked by physicians, is how to increase the metabolic rate as we age. There is still no magic pill that has been invented that will raise the metabolic rate naturally. Recently, a number of supplement companies claim to have invented a number of different herbal combinations and special nutrients, but none have ever proved true in double blind studies performed by a major university or testing laboratory.

Unfortunately for women, men tend to have a higher metabolic rate throughout their lives. This may be due to the male's greater percentage of lean tissue. The more muscle tissue a person has will also increase their metabolic rate.

The thyroid glands level of activity has a direct influence on the basal metabolic rate. The thyroid secretes a hormone, thyroxin, and the less it secretes the lower the energy requirement for the running of the body.

The following is an example of the total energy output by a moderately active homemaker:

Energy for basal metabolism	1,400 calories
Energy for moderate physical activity	500 calories
Energy to burn 2,000 calories	200 calories
	2,100 calories

When more calories are burned than are ingested weight loss will occur.

THE ENERGY BALANCE

Approximately 70% of all food consumed is utilized in keeping the essential life processes going, such as the heart pumping and the liver functioning. The other 30% is turned into "external energy" and used in conscious activities, such as walking, playing sports or working.

The actual energy value of foods is determined by their caloric content. A Kilocalorie is a measure of heat needed to raise the temperature of a liter of water one-degree centigrade (a single calorie is a thousandth of a Kcal).

When we discuss energy balance the input/output theory of weight control usually comes up. This simply means if you burn more calories than you take in you will lose weight. This is of course a true statement, however, it is still the type of calories you consume that will ultimately determine your actual level of health.

EXERCISE

Exercise is a must for everyone, regardless of your age. The type of exercise you do should be one you enjoy doing and one you will continue for an extended period of time. Many people have the initial motivation and good intentions in starting a program but end up doing exercise they don't enjoy and would never stick with.

It is not the intention of the following information to suggest one form of exercise over another, you need to choose the one that fits your lifestyle. The easiest for most people is walking and this chapter will provide you with guidelines of a walking program.

Before starting any exercise program it would be best to have a complete physical from your physician, not just a series of tests by a local athletic club. If you will be walking, swimming, jogging or any very active exercise, a treadmill stress test is a must. A resting cardiogram is a poor test in detecting early heart disease or how your heart will respond to the exertion of exercise.

BENEFITS OF EXERCISE

CARDIOVASCULAR SYSTEM

Exercise increases the efficiency of the cardiovascular system in several ways:

- The heart grows stronger and pumps more blood with each stroke, reducing the number of strokes necessary.

- It increases the number and size of your blood vessels as well as your total blood volume. Enhances oxygenation of your cells.

- It increases your body's maximal oxygen consumption by increasing the efficiency of the red blood cells. By doing this, it improves the overall condition of the body, especially the heart, lungs, and blood vessels.

- It improves the muscle tone of your blood vessels, changing them to strong and firm tissue, possibly reducing blood pressure.

Lungs
Improves the efficiency of the lungs, making them capable of processing more air with less effort.

Aging
Slows the aging process and physical deterioration that accompanies it.

Stress
Helps you relax more easily and develop a better self-image. Relieves the tension and stress of daily living.

Job
Allows you to get more work done at a lower fatigue level.

HEART RATE RESPONSE TO EXERCISE

Resting Heart Rate

The rate will vary widely from individual to individual and also within the individual from one observation to another. It is therefore meaningless to speak of a "normal heart rate." We may say that the average heart rate is 72 beats per minute, but cannot imply that a variation from this figure in either direction is borderline or abnormal.

To determine your own resting heart rate; first take your pulse, 3 times, either radial (side of wrist), or your carotid (side of neck), and count for a total of 60 seconds, average the three figures to give you, your resting pulse rate.

After 10 days of exercising, repeat the procedure to determine your new resting heart rate. If your new rate is lower than the first one, you are experiencing a positive training effect and are starting to get in condition.

FACTORS AFFECTING HEART RATE

AGE   Resting heart rate at birth is approximately 130 beats per minute. It gradually decreases until the teens where it averages out to about 72 beats per minute.

SEX   Resting heart rate in adult females is 5-10 beats faster than the average male.

SIZE   Resting heart rate in animals vary inversely with the size of the species. A canary may have a heart rate of 1,000 beats per minute, while an elephant is only 25 beats per minute.

POSTURE   A change from a sitting to a standing position may increase the heart rate 10-12 beats per minute.

FOOD   The ingestion of food affects the resting heart rate as well as the exercising heart rate. Both rates are higher during digestion than in the pre-consumption period.

EMOTIONS   Increases resting heart rate as well as exercising heart rate. It also tends to slow the recovery rate.

ENVIRONMENT   An increase in ambient temperature causes an increase in the exercising heart rate.

SMOKING   Even one cigarette will cause an increase in the resting heart rate.

AEROBICS AND FITNESS

The term "aerobics" refers to the type of metabolism utilizing oxygen in the production of energy. It relates to modes of training that are designed to improve the efficiency of the body's oxygen exchange system. Thus, delivering more oxygen to the cells while improving the efficiency of the cardiovascular system (heart, lungs, and blood vessels).

The degree to which the cardiovascular system becomes more efficient (and healthier) is dependent upon the total work performed by a particular exercise and its effect on the system.

By gradually increasing the amount and intensity of an exercise program, your fitness level will increase accordingly.

The following is a listing of the most realistic aerobic activities for the average person in their order of aerobic value. Remember, however, these are not recommended prior to a physical evaluation.

EXERCISE	DURATION (MIN.)	TIMES PER WEEK
JOGGING 6 MPH	20	4
BICYCLING 12 MPH	30	5
SWIMMING 25-50 YD/MIN.	20	4
WALKING 4 MPH (O ELEV.)	30	5
ROWING MACHINE	20	5
TENNIS (SINGLES)	45	4
HANDBALL (SINGLES)	30	4
SKATING (ICE OR ROLLER)	45	5
RACQUETBALL (SINGLES)	25	4

FAST AND SLOW TWITCH MUSCLE FIBERS

These muscle fibers are usually utilized first during a sport or exercise until the body determines the need for the "fast twitch muscles." The following are facts apply to the slow twitch muscle fibers:

- Aerobic type muscles, which must burn glucose in the presence of oxygen to produce needed energy.
- Used for long distance endurance, exercises, or sports.
- The number of slow-twitch muscles and the intensity of their movement is usually determined by heredity.
- The size and strength of the fibers can be improved with exercise.
- They are also capable of burning fatty acids, which reduces the body's fat stores.
- The leg muscles of a long distance runner may contain up to 90% of the slow-twitch fibers.

Fast-Twitch Muscle Fibers

Activated when sudden bursts of energy are needed, such as in a "dash" or other fast movement. The following are facts related to fast-twitch muscle fibers:

- These muscles are for the most part anaerobic and burn fuel without the presence of oxygen.
- The leg muscles in world-class tennis players may contain up to 70% fast-twitch muscle fibers.
- As with slow-twitch muscle fibers, the number of fast-twitch muscle fibers is controlled by heredity.
- With training the size of the fibers can be increased and provide faster response.

JUST FOR THE FUN OF IT

SPECIAL EXERCISE CALORIE CHART

Beating around the bush 75
Jogging your memory 125
Jumping to conclusions 100
Climbing the walls 150
Swallowing your pride 50
Passing the buck .25
Grasping at straws 75
Beating your own drum 100
Throwing your weight around 50-300
Dragging your heels 100
Pushing your luck 250
Making mountains out of molehills 500
Spinning your wheels 175
Flying off the handle 225
Hitting the nail on the head 50
Turning the other cheek 75
Wading through paperwork 300
Bending over backwards 75
Jumping on the bandwagon 200
Balancing the books 23
Beating your head against the wall 50
Running around in circles 350
Chewing nails 200
Eating crow 225
Fishing for compliments 50
Tooting your own horn 25
Climbing the ladder of success 750
Pulling out the stoppers 75
Adding fuel to the fire 150
Pouring salt on the wound. 50

HOME FITNESS

Rowing Machines

All-around exerciser: involving the activity of a number of muscle groups. They are excellent for the legs, upper body, and arms. However, they are not recommended for person who is not in condition. They also do not provide the best aerobic workout.

Treadmills

An inexpensive method of exercising is by either walking or jogging. Employs a moving belt, which may be motorized. Most motorized models will allow you to adjust both the speed and elevation. The most frequent complaint is that they tend to become boring after a short period of time. Earphones with music or a TV to watch seems to solve the problem. Computerized models are best.

Mini-Trampolines

Mini-trampolines are a fun way to exercise either indoors or out. They provide an inexpensive aerobic alternative to jogging. Can be used by almost any age group and can provide a fairly good workout if sufficient time is spent.

Stationary Bike (Ergometer)

This by far: the most popular piece of exercise equipment. It provides good aerobic training without the problems that may be caused by the continual pounding of jogging, especially for the unfit. Combining workouts on the rowing machine and the bicycle will provide a well-rounded exercise program.

The cost of the bicycle in most cases will determine the overall quality, ease of making adjustments, and the degree of comfort. Many of the less expensive models do not have adjustable handlebars, which is a comfort feature. Computerized models tend to hold your interest better and give you feedback.

Multi-Gyms

Usually expensive but competition has brought the prices down in recent years. Incorporates a multitude of different exercises into one unit, which makes it handy for home use. Best to try out a unit before buying one, either in a store or a gym. Many of the more unusual units will not hold your interest too long. Be wary of some of the new ones advertised on TV unless you can send it back if you don't like it. Watching a person on TV using the unit is different from you using it in many instances.

FITNESS FACTS:

INJURIES AND PREVENTION

Blisters

Blisters are a common problem, particularly when breaking in a new pair of shoes. Prevention begins with properly fitting shoes and socks that stay in place and do not creep or bunch up. When blisters occur, puncture the edge of the blister with a sterile needle, drain the fluid and apply a topical antiseptic solution, then cover with a Band-Aid.

Arch Conditions

Painful arches are usually the result of improperly fitting shoes, overweight, excessive activity on a hard surface, faulty posture, or fatigue. The symptoms are divided into three stages:

• Slight soreness in the arch area.
• A chronic inflammatory condition that includes soreness, redness, swelling and a slightly visible drop in the arch. See your physician.
• A completely fallen, arch, accompanied by extreme   pain, immobility, and deformity. See your physician.
• Caring for arch disorders should include the following suggestions:

  • Shoes should be properly fitted.
  • Whirlpool hydrotherapy.
  • Ultrasound deep therapy.
  • Arch orthotics.
  • Exercise program, if detected early.

Sprained Ankle

Generally caused by a lateral or medial twist that results in external and internal joint derangement. Sprains may be classified as first, second or third degree. The majority of ankle sprains are the inversion type, resulting in the stretching or tearing of the lateral ligaments. In handling a sprained ankle, these first aid measures should be followed:

• The ankle should be compressed with an ice pack and then elevated for 24 hours.
• If swelling is more than minor or if a fracture is suspected, a physician should be contacted for x-rays.
• With severe ankle sprains, continue cold applications through the second or even the third day.
• Apply heat therapy if swelling has subsided by the third day.

Knee Problem

Although the knee is the largest joint in the body, it is extremely vulnerable to traumatic injuries because of poor bony arrangement. Knee injuries fall mainly into four categories: compression injuries, lateral and medial sprains, torsion injuries, and hyperextending injuries. See your physician.

Lower Back Pain

Lower back pain is usually the result of poor flexibility, weak abdominal and back muscles, and poor posture. Stretching and strengthening exercises, with a conscious effort to improve posture, improves the problem in the majority of cases.

Muscle Soreness

Engagement in activities different from those to which one is normally accustomed often produces muscular soreness. In some cases pain has been reported to occur during the latter stages of high-intensity exercise. More often, it occurs as many as 24-48 hours after the activity. This type of pain is less understood than immediate pain, but it most commonly occurs after an endurance workout. Reports show that the delayed pain to be caused by alterations in the muscle connective tissue (stretching of the elastic components). Recovery; from this type of soreness can be enhanced by warm compresses or warm baths, accompanied by light exercise to help prevent adhesions during the healing process.

Side Stitch

A side stitch usually develops in untrained individuals during aerobic activities. Manifested in mild to agonizing pain in the area of the lower rib cage and may be on either side of the body, but usually the right side. There are several explanations for this occurrence, none of which is completely satisfactory. It is probable that all of the following factors contribute to the discomfort:

- Accumulation of metabolic wastes (lactic acid) in the diaphragm.
- Severe shaking of the abdominal contents, which causes pain in the supporting structures.
- Formation of gas in the ascending colon.
- Reduced blood flow to the affected area due to the rerouting of blood to other areas.

Relief is usually accelerated by the application of pressure on the affected side while the exercise is continued. If the pain becomes too severe, the alternative is to terminate the workout and rest.

Achilles Tendon Rupture

This usually follows a history of chronic inflammation and gradual degeneration caused by micro-tears. When the rupture occurs, the individual complains of a sudden snap or that something has hit them in the lower leg. Severe pain, point tenderness, swelling, and discoloration are usually associated with the trauma. Signs of a rupture are obvious indentations at the tendon site or a positive Thompson Test.

Achilles Tendon Bursitis and Tendinitis

Bursitis and tendinitis usually occur from the over-stretching of the Achilles tendon, resulting in a constant inflammatory condition of the Achilles bursar. The condition is chronic, developing gradually over a period of time, and takes many days to heal. An excellent therapeutic approach is ultrasound (electrical heat transfer). Activity should be held to a minimum, and heel lifts should be placed in the shoe to relieve the Achilles tendon of as much tension as possible. After a workout, the tendon should be cooled with ice packs or ice massage. Gradual heel cord stretching is recommended.

Shin Splints

These are characterized by pain and irritation in the shin region of the leg, and are usually attributed to an inflammation localized mostly in the tendon of the tibialis posterior and flexor digitorum longus. Inflammation in this area is often a mystery. Speculation of cause include: faulty posture alignment, falling arches, muscle fatigue, overuse stress, body chemical imbalance or a lack of reciprocal muscle coordination between the anterior and posterior aspects of the leg. These factors singly or in combination, may contribute to shin splints.

While rest is the only sure cure, limited exercise is possible with an ice massage and a leg wrap. Prevention of shin splints; can be accomplished by using proper footwear, running on soft surfaces, stretching, and strengthening the surrounding musculature.

WALKING NECESSARY TO WALK OFF COMMON SNACK FOODS

The following information will provide the walking distance required to work off the calories of a number of common snacks and foods.

SNACK	SERVING	CALORIES	MILES
THAT LITTLE SANDWICH			
Ham	$^1/_2$ oz. w/butter	335	5.8
Cheese	$^1/_2$ oz. w/mayo	400	6.7
Peanut Butter/jelly	2 Tbs. peanut butter 1 Tbl. jelly	425	7.4
Hamburger on bun	3 inch patty	445	8.0
Tortilla w/cheese	1 oz. cheese	190	3.2
BEVERAGES			
Carb. soft drink	12 oz. can	160	2.7
Chocolate malt	12 oz. glass	485	8.2
Ice cream soda	12 oz. glass	290	4.7
Milk/whole	8 oz. glass	160	2.7
Tea or coffee (w/2T cream & 2t sugar)	8 oz. cup	90	1.6

Beer	12 oz. can	165	2.8
High Ball (w/ginger ale)	8 oz. glass	140	2.8
Martini	Average	160	2.7
Manhattan	Average	175	3.0
Sherry	4 oz. glass	120	2.1
Scotch, Bourbon,	1 shot glass	80	1.3

FRUITS

Apple	1 medium	90	1.5
Orange	1 medium	85	1.4
Pear	1 medium	100	1.7
Grapes	25 medium	70	1.2
Banana	1-6 inch long	100	1.7
Date	1 medium	27	0.4

SALTED NUTS

Almonds	10	130	2.2
Pecans	10	150	2.5
Cashews	10	60	1.0
Walnuts	1 oz. shelled	175	2.9
Peanut	1 medium	6	0.1

CANDIES

Chocolate bar	1 1/4 oz.	185	3.1
BonBon	1 pc.	90	1.5
Caramel	1 pc. 3/4 inch	40	0.7
Jelly Bean	1 avg.	6	0.1

DESSERTS

Doughnut	1 medium	140	2.3
Ice Cream Cone	1 scoop	190	3.2
Ice Cream Sundae	2 scoops w/toppings	400	6.7
Cake (layer)	1 avg. piece	290	4.8
Pie (fruit)	1/6 pie	340	5.7
Cream Puff	4 inch diameter	365	6.1
Brownie	1 medium	300	5.0
Graham Cracker	1	42	0.7

MISCELLANEOUS

Potato Chips	10 medium	115	1.8
Popcorn(w/o butter)	1 cup	60	1.0
1 tablespoon butter modest amount for popcorn	1 Tbl.	85	1.4
Saltine Crackers	4	50	0.8

MIDNIGHT ICE BOX RAID

Piece of chicken	1oz.	105	1.8
Chicken leg	1 average	85	1.5
Hard Boiled Egg	1 medium	80	1.3
Jello	1/2 cup	70	1.2

EXERCISE AND CALORIES

The purpose of the following information is to create an awareness of which foods are higher in calories and the number of minutes needed to work off the foods. The information is based on a 150-pound adult.

	Calories	Walking 3 MPH	Bicycling 15 MPH	Jogging 5 MPH
BREAD & CEREALS				
Raisin Bran (1/2 cup)	73	15	7	10
Special K (1/2 cup)	30	6	3	4
Cornbread (2" sq.)	107	21	10	13
White Bread (1 sl.)	62	12	6	8
WW Bread (1 sl.)	56	11	5	7
Donut, iced (1 med.)	150	30	14	19
Blueberry Muffin	110	22	10	14
Cinnamon Bun	158	32	14	20
Pancake (med.)	110	22	10	14
Waffle (med.)	165	34	15	20
White Rice (3/4 cup)	103	21	9	13
Egg Noodles (1/4 cup)	70	14	6	9
Air Popcorn (1 cup)	54	11	5	7
Popcorn/oil (1 cup)	82	16	7	10
Graham Cracker (1)	30	6	3	4
Macaroni/cheese(1 C)	530	110	57	70
Spagh/meat balls (1 C)	310	68	35	46
Taco/beef (3 oz.)	195	45	22	30
Saltine Cracker (1)	14	3	1	2
MEATS				
Bacon/cooked (2 sl.)	100	20	8	12
Beef Hash (1/2 C)	230	46	21	29
Reg. Hamburger	225	45	20	28
Lean Hamburger	140	28	13	18
Beef Pot Pie (med.)	445	90	40	55
Chili/beans/meat(5 oz)	185	39	17	25
Hot Dog/plain	125	25	12	16
Ham Slice (2 oz)	185	35	18	22
Lamb (3 oz)	300	60	25	35
Meat Loaf (3 oz)	285	61	30	40
Chicken TV dinner	542	108	49	68
Bologna (1 sl)	66	13	6	8
Sausage (1 reg link)	95	19	9	12
T-Bone Steak (4 oz)	175	35	22	22

FISH/SHELLFISH

Deviled Crab (1)	188	38	17	24
Baked Flounder (3 oz)	200	41	19	28
Broiled Lobster (1 med)	310	62	28	39
Fried Oysters (7)	235	48	22	30
Broiled Salmon (4 oz)	200	45	23	29
Fried Shrimp (3 oz)	205	40	16	22
Tuna/water (4 oz)	127	26	11	16
Tuna/oil (4 oz)	205	49	19	29
Anchovies (3)	21	4	2	3

POULTRY

Fried Chicken (1/2)	460	100	45	58
Fried Chicken Leg	150	30	13	19
Roast Turkey (1 sl)	80	16	8	10

NUTS

Almonds (14)	90	18	8	11
Cashews (7)	84	17	8	11
Peanuts (1 Tbl)	86	18	8	11
Peanut Butter (1 Tbl)	88	19	9	12
Pecans (6)	100	21	9	13
Sunflower Seeds (3 oz)	502	110	50	65

PREPARED SALADS

Coleslaw (1 cup)	79	21	10	15
Carrot/Raisin (3 oz)	150	31	14	19
Macaroni Salad (1 cup)	335	67	30	41
Potato Salad (1 cup)	200	40	19	24
Salad Dressing (1 Tbl)	71	14	6	9

DAIRY PRODUCTS

Milk/whole (1 cup)	160	32	14	20
Milk/non-fat (1 cup)	105	21	10	13
Buttermilk (1 cup)	88	18	8	11
Amer. Cheese (1 oz)	110	21	10	14
Cottage Cheese (1/2 C)	120	29	14	18
Ice Cream (1/2 cup)	225	41	20	27
Yogurt/non-fat (1 C)	122	24	11	15

SOUPS

Cream of Mush. (1 C)	150	30	14	19
Chicken Noodle (1 C)	60	12	7	8
Split Pea (1 C)	120	24	11	15
Tomato (1 C)	73	15	7	9

SWEET TREATS

Chocolate Bar	215	44	20	27
Milky Way (reg)	285	57	26	37
Choc. Chip Cookies (3)	150	30	14	19
Banana Split (2 scoop)	600	120	54	74

Eclair	300	60	27	37
Apple Pie (1 slice)	390	79	35	48
Brownie (1 sq.)	150	30	14	19

BEVERAGES

Beer (12 oz)	230	42	20	53
Lite Beer (12 oz)	100	20	9	13
Brandy (3 ½ oz)	75	15	7	9
Martini (3 ½ oz)	140	28	13	18
Wine (4 oz)	110	22	10	14
Champagne (4 oz)	85	17	8	10
Milkshake (8 oz)	420	85	38	55
Eggnog (8 oz)	235	48	22	29
Cola Soda (12 oz)	155	31	14	21

RESTAURANT SANDWICHES

Club (3 sl bread)	600	120	59	78
Egg Salad	280	56	25	35
Tuna Salad	280	56	25	35
BLT	285	58	27	39

VEGETABLES

Asparagus (½ cup)	17	3	2	3
Broccoli (½ cup)	26	5	3	3
Cabbage (½ cup)	20	4	2	3
Sweet Corn (1 ear)	96	20	9	12
Sweet Pickle (1 lg)	140	30	14	18
Baked Potato (1 med)	100	20	10	14
French Fries (10 avg)	140	30	12	17
Mashed Pot. (½ cup)	90	16	7	10
Potato Chips (sm bag)	115	22	10	14

FRUITS

Apple (med)	50	10	4	6
Banana (1 sm)	88	17	8	12
Cantaloupe (¼ melon)	45	9	4	6
Grapefruit (½ sm)	40	8	4	5
Orange (1 sm)	50	10	5	7
Watermelon (1 cup)	45	9	4	6

CHAPTER 17

VITAMINS, ANTIOXIDANTS & MORE

WHY WE NEED SUPPLEMENTS

How often have we heard that if we eat a balanced diet with all the food groups in the right proportions, we will be able to obtain all the necessary nutrients our bodies need. We are all tired of listening to this statement from professionals who have a limited education in the field of nutrition or have been brainwashed to really believe this is possible.

The above statement was, however, true 70 years ago before we were bombarded with more environmental insults than our bodies knew how to cope with. The following information will alert you to the all the reasons why we cannot possibly remain in optimum health without taking supplements.

Every week on television there seems to be another show telling of another problem with our food supply. We are not inspecting our foods properly due to lack of inspectors, our fruits and vegetables are grown in soils that are nutrient-deficient due to the depletion of trace minerals from over-farming.

Our products are stored too long before they are sold and many of the natural nutrients are processed out before they reach us. No one will ever convince me that they are enriching our foods sufficiently to provide us with anywhere near the original levels.

We use preservatives and coloring agents that are borderline chemical agents and many have been proven to cause cancer in laboratory animals. We don't have time to eat a balanced diet and we kill off all the enzymes with heat before we eat the food.

Then we take a supplement that has probably lost a percentage of its potency and has a low level of "biologic activity" to save a few dollars. Many supplement products are just not active enough and cannot provide you with the level of nutrients you buy them for.

The following information will give you some insight into the "real" world of nutrition and the many factors that relate to your obtaining the level of nutrients from the foods you purchase. It will also provide some additional information regarding the need for supplementation in relation to a variety of lifestyle factors.

DIGESTIVE ENZYMES

These are proteins that are necessary to breakdown foodstuffs after we ingest them. Our bodies make enzymes, however, many people do not have adequate enzymes produced to handle the variety and volume of foods we consume. These products contain additional enzymes that are used to assist the body in breaking down proteins, carbohydrates, and fats into small sub-units that can more easily be absorbed.

LOSS OF NUTRIENT AVAILABILITY IN FOODS

SOME REASONS FOR NUTRIENT LOSSES

Temperature changes take their toll on nutrients. The following is an example of why these losses occur:

FRIED FOODS

The higher the temperature, and the longer the food is fried, the higher the nutrient loss. Most frying temperatures reach 360° F making an oil such as canola oil best for frying because of its high smoke point of over 400° F. This allows canola oil to be used for a longer period of time before breaking down and smoking.

CANNED FOODS

Vitamin and mineral potency losses occur mainly from cooking and the sterilization process, which can involve temperatures of 240° F. or higher for up to 30 minutes.

FROZEN FOODS

It will depend on whether these foods were cooked before being frozen. This determines the level of nutrient loss from processing. In many instances the higher quality foods and better appearing foods are sold fresh, while lower quality ones are usually processed for frozen foods.

DEHYDRATED FOODS

If these are processed using a high quality product, the nutritional content for the most part will be retained. However, many companies choose to use lower quality goods since they cannot be distinguished from the quality ones. The most commonly used method of dehydrating foods use temperatures of 300° F. or higher. Air dehydrating takes too long.

DAIRY PRODUCTS

The pasteurization process takes its toll on nutrients. Many vitamins either lose their potency or are totally destroyed. When dairy products are homogenized, the process designed breaks down the normal-sized fat particles and may allow the formation of an enzyme called "xanthane oxidase." Studies performed in Canada stated that this enzyme; may enter the bloodstream and destroy specific chemicals that would ordinarily provide protection for the smaller coronary arteries.

REFINING OUT AND REPLACING NUTRIENTS

Bread is a good example, many nutrients are processed out and only a few replaced. Vitamin D is added to milk and almost all breakfast cereals are fortified unless they contain the whole grain. Vitamin C and calcium are added to numerous products.

NOTE:
White and wheat flours (not the 100% or whole grain type) may lose up to 90% of its vitamin E potency during processing. Cereal products, especially rice, may lose up to 70% of their vitamin E.

CANNED AND PACKAGED PRODUCTS

The Length of time on the shelf of a supermarket as well as possible warehousing time may result in reduced potencies of many vitamins and minerals.

FRUITS AND VEGETABLES

Frequently these are picked before they are fully ripened,then allowed to ripen while being transported to the supermarket. Produce departments tend to cut a number of fruits into smaller, more salable pieces. This causes more of their surface to be exposed to the effects of air and light. Oxidation takes place more rapidly, thus reducing their nutrient content.

ROTATION OF FOODS

When bringing home any food, it should be dated and rotated. This is one of the more frequent mistakes most people make. Nutrients are only potent for a period of time, which varies with every product.

WAREHOUSING

Most supermarket foods are warehoused before being shipped to the market. The time they are delayed will have a lot to do with the ultimate level of nutrients.

RESTAURANTS

To save money restaurants purchase in large quantities, possibly resulting in long storage times before the food is served. Most fast food restaurants avoid this problem since they serve a great number of people.

NOTE:
In a recent study it was found that some oranges from supermarkets were found to contain no vitamin C content, while a fresh picked one contains approximately 80 mg.. This is due to a number of factors previously mentioned.

Tests have shown that a potato, which has been in storage for up to 4-6 months, will lose at least 50% of its vitamin C content. The nutritional information panels on foods now deduct 25% of the nutrient value of that food to allow for storage, effects of light, type of packaging material, transportation times, processing, preservation chemicals, and cooking.

SOIL PROBLEM

Only the minerals that are crucial to crop growth are replaced back into the soil, these usually only include phosphorus, potassium, and nitrates. Selenium, a trace mineral may vary by a factor of 200 in soils in the continental United States. You never know how much selenium you are really getting from the foods that should contain an adequate amount. Wheat is a good example and may contain from 50mcg to 800mcg depending on where it is grown.

Two other important minerals chromium and zinc are also critically deficient in the soil. The problem is significant and is presently under study by the USDA.

MEAL PLANNING

Too few people plan their meals in advance. This results in poor combinations of foods, leading to inadequate vitamin and mineral intake.

SMOKING AND VITAMIN C

Recent studies have shown that smoker's require approximately 40% more vitamin C than non-smokers to achieve adequate blood levels. Every cigarette may reduce bodily stores by about 30mg, which means that a pack of cigarettes requires at least a 600mg increase in vitamin C intake.

SMOG

All major cities in the United States have some form of chemical air pollution. This pollution will effect your lungs' capacity to deliver oxygen efficiently to the cells of the body. The antioxidant vitamins A, C, E, selenium, the mineral OptiZinc™, and proanthocyanidin have proved to be effective in combating some of the effects of chemical pollution.

SMOKE

The smoke from cigarettes, cigars, and pipes all effect the oxygen-carrying efficiency of your red blood cells. Smoke contains carbon monoxide, which may compete for the site on the red blood cell that should be always carrying oxygen. This is one reason why smokers are short-winded, a percentage of their red blood cells are carrying carbon monoxide instead of the needed oxygen.

DAIRY PRODUCT INTOLERANCE

The mechanism to produce the enzyme to breakdown lactase loses it efficiency over time in many people. This may lead to a reduction of available calcium by not eating dairy products. Dark   green leafy vegetables will help supply calcium and a new product "Lactaid" will assist the body in breaking down lactase.

HORMONAL CHANGES

- Aging and hormonal changes may lead to an increase in the loss of calcium, and supplementation, especially of calcium should be considered.
- Vitamin B6 absorption is effected by the hydrazines in mushrooms. If you are taking birth control pills, it may be best to only consume mushrooms occasionally.
- Boiling any food for more than 5-10 minutes will destroy 100% of the vitamin B and C content.
- Make sure you cook all fish, shellfish, brussels sprouts, and red cabbage. They contain thiaminase, a chemical, which may destroy the B vitamins in these foods. Cooking inactivates the thiaminase, however, that will also kill the B vitamins.
- The tannins in teas and red wines may interfere with the utilization of iron, thiamin and B12. Moderation is the key word. Iron absorption can be also be affected by coffee consumption and may leach magnesium out of the body. Vitamin C is required to assist in the metabolism of iron. If it is not present in adequate amounts, less than 30% of the ingested iron, will be utilized by the body.
- When taking a vitamin C supplement, remember that if it isn't time-released, your body is only capable of metabolizing about 250mg per hour. A 500mg in a non-time release is all that should be taken.
- Studies have shown that PABA may retard or even aid in returning original hair color.
- Vitamins A, D, E and K are best absorbed in the intestines when a small amount of fat is present. If you are taking a vitamin E supplement: as a single supplement it would be best to take it with a small amount of 2% milk.
- Americans spent $4.9 billion on nutritional supplements in 1999.
- The American Medical Society cited studies that revealed eating excessive amounts of foods that are high in vitamin A, such as; liver, carrots, and cantaloupe, may result in headaches and nausea.
- A good laxative would be to take one teaspoon of crystalline vitamin C when you first awake with 8oz of water. This will usually result in a bowel movement within 30 minutes.
- Studies show that Caucasian men and African-American women lose calcium stores at a faster pace than the rest of the population after age 30. For Caucasian women it begins at age 18. African-American men do not seem to have the problem.

GETTING THE MOST

- Calcium supplements are best absorbed when taken with meals, since the calcium likes the acid medium. Calcium is also best utilized by the bones when boron is present. The better sources of boron may be found in prunes, raisins, almonds, peanuts, dates, and honey. Studies have also shown that if you consume a small amount of sugar the absorption rate will improve.
- Vitamin supplements will maintain their freshness longer if stored in the refrigerator. Most will maintain a good level of potency for about 2 years.
- Aspirin tends to reduce the effectiveness of vitamin C.
- Vitamin A is important for a healthy immune system as well as assisting the body in the retention of vitamin C and zinc metabolism.

THE UNREAL VITAMINS

The following are a few of the vitamin names that have been devised by the health food industry to associate the word "vitamin" with a variety of different products. None of these are true vitamins.

Vitamin F . . . .Supposed to stand for unsaturated fatty acids.
Vitamin O . . . .Stands for oxygen when added to a product.
Vitamin P . . . .Stands for plant pigment (flavenoid)
Vitamin T . . . .Derived from egg yolks and sesame seeds.
Vitamin U . . . .The "U" is for ulcer and is supposed to relieve ulcer pain.
Vitamin B17 . .Designation for laetrile from apricot pits.

The 13 true vitamins are A,C,D,E and K. The B vitamins are a group of 8 vitamins consisting of thiamin B1, riboflavin B2, niacin B3, folic acid, pantothenic acid, biotin, pyrodoxine B6 and B12.

HIGH PROTEIN INTAKE = DANGER

Can shorten life expectancy, increase the risk of cancer, deplete calcium from bones, can cause fluid imbalances, may stress and damage the liver and kidneys, cause a hazard to premature infants, one cause of obesity, and will increase the need for vitamin B6.

Studies are being done relating low vitamin D levels to breast cancer. Areas of the country with low sunlight levels seem to have a higher incidence of breast cancer.

Beta-carotene, which assists the body to produce vitamin A is only available from plants while, the actual vitamin A is only available from animal sources.

VITAMIN ROBBERS

The following information will provide information regarding some of the environmental factors, drugs, and everyday product use that can significantly affect the potency and availability of many nutrients. The awareness of these factors should assist you in making choices regarding your supplement program.

VITAMIN/MINERAL	ROBBER
Vitamin A	Mineral oil, air pollution/smog, fertilizer nitrates, antacids, corticosteroids.
Vitamin D	Anti-convulsive drugs (dilantin), consumption, alcohol, stressful situations, oral contraceptives. mineral oil, antacids, oral contraceptives, alcohol.
Thiamin B1	Antibiotics, excess heat/cooking, sugar
Riboflavin B2	Antibiotics, exposure to light, diuretics, reserpine.

Niacin	Excessive heat, alcohol, most illnesses reduce intestinal absorption, nitrites and nitrates, penicillin.
PABA	Sulfa drugs.
Pantothenic Acid	Methyl bromide insecticide (fumigant for foods).
Pyradoxine B6	Aging causes levels to decline after 50, steroids, hormones, hydralazine (hypertension drug), excessive heat, food processing, corticosteroids, hydralazine.
Folic Acid	Oral contraceptives, stress situations, vitamin C deficiency.
Vitamin B12	Prolonged iron deficiency, stress, oral contraceptives.
Biotin	Excess heat, antibiotics, sulfa drugs,avidin in raw egg white, oral contraceptives.
Calcium	Antacids, aspirin, corticosteroids, diuretics, lidocaine.
Choline	Sugar consumption, alcohol.
Inositol	Antibiotics.
Magnesium	Thiazides, alcohol, diuretics.
Vitamin C	Overexertion, fatigue, stress, aspirin, smoking, alcohol, corticosteroids, antihistamines, fluoride, oral contraceptives, barbituates.
Vitamin E	Oral contraceptives, food processing, rancid fats, mineral oil.
Vitamin K	Antibiotics, mineral oil, radiation, anticoagulants, phenobarbital, alcohol.

SUPPLEMENTS FOR THE NEW MILLENNIUM

STEROLS/STEROLINS

This is a unique nutrient with numerous studies relating the benefits and the sterols/sterolins will probably be the hottest new supplement of the 21st century. The nutrient is composed mainly of plant fats (sterols) and glucosides (sterolins). The studies are relating to increasing the efficiency of the immune system to fight disease and keep you healthy. The benefits related to by the studies range anywhere from slowing the advance of AIDS to reducing blood pressure, with an all-natural product that will be classified as a food.

The product, to be most effective, according to studies, should contain a 5-8:1 ratio, which simply means that the amount of plant fat contained in the product needs one unit of sterolins to activate and assist in the metabolism of 5-8 units of sterols in the products being manufactured. Plant fats are easily destroyed by a number of factors and our intake has been well below the level that would assist the body in keeping the immune system at its optimum level of health. The most active source is the African potato/hypoxis plant.

PHYTOCHEMICALS

These chemical extracts from fruits and vegetables are becoming the latest fad in prevention. Basically, they are the biologically active, non-nutritive substances, found in plants that give them their color, flavor, odor, and provides them with their natural defense system against diseases. Simply put, these are not nutrients, nor vitamins or minerals, just chemical compounds that exist in fruits and vegetables. Their new name in many publications is "Nutraceuticals." They have been known to exist for years, but never received much press or attention until recent studies started linking then to cancer prevention in laboratory animals.

Studies regarding phytochemicals are presently being conducted by numerous agencies and universities including The National Cancer Society and The National Academy of Science. Phytochemicals are presently showing results in animals, arresting cancer in all stages of cellular development. Exactly which phytochemicals will be beneficial to humans and in what types of cancer, are questions that will take years to answer.

We have always known that whole grains, fruits, and vegetables should be consumed in adequate amounts on a daily basis for optimum health, and that cancer was not as prevalent in the early part of the century as it is today. The possible explanation is that our grandparents ate a healthier diet with more unprocessed foods and more fruits and vegetables. The naturally occurring compounds in these foods provided a degree of "natural" protection.

Cancer has only become more prevalent since the 1940's when we learned how to process foods, can them, use chemicals more efficiently in our foods and heat them until almost all the nutrients were either lost or biochemically altered. Phytochemicals may, however, be one answer to reducing the incidence of cancer.

One very important factor is that phytochemicals are not destroyed by cooking or processing to any great degree. The problem is that we just don't eat enough of them. If that is the case then we should consider taking a "Nutraceutical" supplement or any supplement that contains these phytochemicals or phytoextracts.

There are over 100,000 phytochemicals and the more sophisticated our analysis equipment becomes over time, we will probably identify even more. The following list provides the most current 1999 information obtainable on the more potent and important of these extractions. All information has been taken from laboratory animal testing only.

PHYTOCHEMICALS IN FRUITS, VEGETABLES AND HERBS

FOOD	PHYTOCHEMICAL
Broccoli, cauliflower, Brussels sprouts, kale,	SULFORAPHANE Activates enzyme that aids in turnips. removing carcinogens from the body.
	DITHIOLTHIONES Triggers production of enzymes that may block carcinogens from damaging DNA.

These phytochemicals have shown special cancer fighting benefits by inhibiting cancer of the breast tumors in laboratory animals. Cooking methods such as microwaving and steaming increases the availability of the phytochemical.

Broccoli has 40 phytochemicals.

Sweet potatoes, yams, artichokes, red grapes, red wine, strawberries.	FLAVONOIDS/POLYPHENOLS Attaches to cancer cells and stops hormones from attaching.

May reduce the risk of cancer by attaching to free radicals and flushing them out of the body, this may also reduce the risk of cardiovascular diseases. This phytochemical is a part of the red wine/lower heart disease factor in France. However, it would be wise to avoid the red wine and consume the foods until additional studies are more conclusive. Recommendations are 1/3 cup per day.

| Cabbage, turnips, dark green leafy vegetables. | INDOLES Studies show that they reduce the risk of breast cancer. |

Tends to improve immune system function and may protect against cancer by allowing the body to eliminate toxins more easily. Stimulates the production of an enzyme that may make estrogen less effective, which may give a degree of protection against breast and ovarian cancers.

| Soybeans, dried beans, mung bean sprouts. | GENISTEIN Cuts off the blood supply to tumors cells by retarding their capillary growth. |

This phytochemical is called a "phytoestrogen" and may offer protection against breast cancer, osteoporosis, heart disease, and most female hormones associated problems. Additional phytochemicals found in soybeans may help reduce blood cholesterol levels and slow replication of cancer cells. Three four-ounce servings of "tofu" or three cups of soy milk daily is recommended.

| Chili peppers | CAPSAICIN Stops toxic molecules from attaching to DNA. |

An anti-inflammatory substance that prevents carcinogens from attaching to DNA and discourages the growth and replication of cancer cells. Other potential uses are killing bacteria that may cause stomach ulcers and as a treatment for bronchitis and colds.

Should be consumed in moderation: as red chili peppers tend to stimulate gastric acid causing indigestion and general stomach irritation. Recommendations are no more than 2-4 small peppers per day if tolerated well.

| Citrus fruit | LIMONENE Activates enzyme that disposes of carcinogens. |

The active substance d-limonene, has shown to offer protection against breast cancer in laboratory animals. It also increases the production of additional enzymes that may assist the immune system in disposing of carcinogens. Future studies may also show that this phytochemical will actually reduce plaque in arteries. The pulpier the product, the better. Recommendations are 16-24 ounces of pulpy orange juice daily or 3-4 pieces of citrus fruit.

Orange juice has 59 known phytochemicals.

Apples/fruits	CAFFEIC ACID Increases the solubility of toxins so they can be flushed from the body.
	FERULIC ACID Binds to nitrates in stomach.
Grapes, strawberries, raspberries.	ELLAGIC ACID May prevent carcinogens from entering DNA.
Garlic, onions, leeks.	ALLYLIC SULFIDE Detoxifies carcinogens.
Chives	ALLIUM COMPOUNDS Slows reproduction of carcinogens, allows more time for them to be destroyed.

Recent studies show that these vegetables may lower HDL (bad cholesterol) and detoxify the body by increasing the production of glutathione S-transferase, which may cause carcinogens to be excreted more easily. When combined with the mineral selenium it may have an effect on breast cancer. May reduce incidence of heart disease by having a mild blood thinning effect and may decrease the risk of stomach cancers.

Garlic and onions have 50 phytochemicals.

When garlic is processed, it releases the sulfur compound, which can stimulate immune responses. Too much garlic powder may interfere with anticoagulants and cause stomach upsets.

Recommendations are 2-4 fresh cloves of garlic or $\frac{1}{2}$ cup of raw onion daily. Keep mints handy!

Grains, especially rye, wheat, rice, sesame seeds,	PHYTIC ACID Binds to iron, thus reducing a and peanuts.free radical production mechanism.

Studies are being conducted relating to the prevention of colon cancer and to reduce the severity of intestinal cancers.

Tomatoes, green peppers	P-COUMARIC & CHLORGENIC ACIDS Kills cancer-forming substances in their formation stages. This group contains over 10,000 phytochemicals.
Carrots, seaweed, squash, peaches, red, yellow, dark green vegetables.	ALPHA-CAROTENE/BETA-CAROTENE Fights free radicals which may invade the DNA causing an abnormal cell to be produced.

Tends to improve vitamin A effectiveness and improves immune system responses as well as decreasing the risk of lung cancer in laboratory mice. Carrots should be cleaned thoroughly and left unpeeled to preserve the phytochemicals. Recommendation is 1-2 carrots or one cup of seaweed daily.

Licorice root	GLYCYRRHIZIN & TRITERPENOIDS Has disease fighting properties. Still under investigation.

Increases the effectiveness of the immune system and tends to slow the rate at which cancer cells replicate. Also, useful in treating gastrointestinal problems and ulcers. Contains antibacterial properties and helps fight tooth decay and gingivitis. Prevents breast cancer in laboratory animals by activating the production of liver enzymes, reducing the level of tumor-promoting estrogens.

Persons with high blood pressure should not eat licorice. Anise, a licorice flavoring does not contain the phytochemical, only licorice root.

Green tea/black tea (Not herbal teas)	POLYPHENOL CATECHINS AND THEAFLAVIN Studies are ongoing regarding cancer fighting abilities.

May have a tendency to increase fat metabolism as well as increasing the effectiveness of the immune system and lowering cholesterol. The phenols have been found in recent studies to protect tissues from oxidation.

Tea must be brewed for at least 5-10 minutes to get maximum catechin content. Excessive consumption may cause stomach upsets and provide a large dose of caffeine. Moderation is the key

Rosemary

CARNOSOL
An antioxidant.

Tends to reduce the development of certain types of tumors and may protect fats in the body from oxidizing. May be used freely on salads or other foods.

Flaxseed

LIGANS
Antioxidant of which flaxseed is the pre-cursor.

Flaxseed contains elements that are capable of producing "ligans" a potent antioxidant, it also contains omega-3 fatty acids which may have anti-cancer properties. Recommendations are to use ground, fortified flaxseed with B6 and zinc added. Daily dose: in 1 tablespoon of grain or 1 teaspoon of oil.

Red grapefruit, tomatoes, watermelon, apricots.

LYCOPENE
An antioxidant.

May decrease the risk of colon and bladder cancer in laboratory mice as well as reducing the risk of heart disease. Protects DNA and cells against damage from free radicals. Fruits should be uncooked and as fresh as possible. New 1999 studies are being conducted that may prove lycopene to be one of the best phytonutrients in the prevention of many types of cancer. One cup daily is recommended.

Yellow squash, spinach, collard, mustard, and turnip greens.

LUTEIN/ZEAXANTHIN
Slows growth of cancer cells.

Reduces the risk of lung cancer, strengthens the immune system and may have a role in the prevention of colon, prostate, and esophageal cancers. Steam the greens in a small amount of water for a short period of time. Two-thirds of a cup daily is recommended.

Cranberry juice

ANTHOCYANINS
May prevent and cure urinary tract problems.

Best to use unsweetened cranberry juice to water or tea. Two 8-ounce glasses per day is the recommendation.

Ginger root	GINGEROL Relieves motion sickness.

Has anti-inflammatory properties and may relieve symptoms of headaches. One-half teaspoon of powdered root or 1 teaspoon of fresh ginger daily. Tea can be made by simmering several slices in 2-3 cups of water for 8-10 minutes then strain.

Horseradish, cabbage, turnips.	PHENETHYL ISOTHIOCYANATES Tends to reduce tumor growth.

Activates enzymes that block carcinogens from damaging the DNA. May inhibit cancer of the lungs.

Kidney beans, chickpeas, soybeans, lentils. may even prevent	SAPONINS Slows the growth of cancer cells and them from replicating.

Basil, carrots, parsley, mint, caraway seeds, citrus fruits, cabbage.	MONOTERPENES May interfere with the replication of cancer cells.

Nutraceuticals, at present, are regulated by the FDA as dietary supplements only and are not classified as drugs. They are extractions from natural foods, to date have had no definitive extensive studies completed, and all claims made for them as mentioned above are still speculative. Studies that have been reported have all been on laboratory animals. Hopefully, more human studies will be forthcoming in the very near future.

Claims made for products that offer cancer protection and cure should be viewed with caution. Products that contain herbal or botanical ingredients should indicate the part of the plant the product was produced from. Be sure labels list all the ingredients that are present in significant amounts.

A future statement that may appear on these products may read; "This food product is not intended to diagnose, treat, cure or prevent any disease." Phytochemicals in the future will be transferred to different foods and produce foods that will be called "functional foods." The Functional Foods for Health project is presently underway at the University of Illinois.

Phyto-Fortified Foods (FFH) will be the new wave of the future.

PROANTHOCYANIDIN (PAC)

A relatively new antioxidant that may be purchased under a brand name (Pycnogenol) or by its generic name (proanthocyanidin) has only recently appeared in many products. It is a natural plant product, originally extracted from the bark of pine trees. However, it is now being extracted from grape seeds as well as pine bark. The substance is found in many natural foods, however, it is relatively expensive to extract from most of them.

Proanthocyanidin, is stated to be 20 times more powerful than vitamin C and 50 times more powerful than vitamin E. It also, may have the ability to protect a number of antioxidants from being destroyed before they are able to perform their functions or be utilized by the cell.

PAC is water, soluble and has the ability to be absorbed and utilized by the cell very shortly after ingestion. PAC remains in the body for three days circulating in body fluids and is gradually eliminated. If taken regularly, cells will acquire a saturation level which provides a continuum of beneficial antioxidant activity.

PAC is one of the most efficient free radical scavengers known. It has the unique ability to actually adhere to collagen (connective tissue) fibers and ward off the potential damage that might be done by circulating free radicals. This function may be the emphasis of future studies that relate to aging of the skin and joint diseases, such as arthritis.

CAROTENOIDS

Fruits and vegetables contain over 500 carotenoids. Carotenoids is a pigment that gives food their color. About 10% of the carotenoids will convert to vitamin A and provide 25% of the bodies usable vitamin A. Studies are continuing and the future may show that carotenoids are more effective when taken together as a potent antioxidant.

Beta-carotene may not be the "magic bullet" to slow down or stop a cancer cell from replicating, however, a combination of carotenoids may provide the protection we are hoping for. One of the more interesting findings is that carotenoids improve communications between premalignant cells and normal cells. Tumor growth is slowed when they receive regulating signals from the normal cells.

Animal studies have shown that when a combination of carotenoids were given there was a decrease in the number of cancer cells.

A recent study showed that people eating cooked (boiled) carrots and spinach actually have twice the blood levels of carotenoids than people who ate the two vegetables raw. Many vegetables do not release adequate carotenoids until they are processed.

MAJOR CAROTENOIDS

CAROTENOID	FOOD SOURCE	POSSIBLE BENEFIT
Alpha carotene	Carrots	Activity of vitamin A decreased the risk of lung cancer and slowed the growth of cancerous cells in mice as well as increasing immune system response.
Beta-carotene	Broccoli, cantaloupe, carrots	Same response as alpha-carotene, with the additional decrease of colon, bladder, and skin cancers in mice.
Beta-cryptoxanthin	Mangos, oranges, papayas, tangerines	Vitamin A activity.
Canthaxanthin	Natural food color added To jellies, jams, soft drinks, and tomato sauce	Found to slow skin cancer in mice as well as slowing the growth of cancer cells and improving immune response in mice.
Lutein	Broccoli, dark green leafy vegetables	Decreased the risk of lung cancer in mice.
Lycopene	Tomatoes, tomato products	Decreased the risk of colon and bladder cancer and slowed the replication of cancer cells in mice.
Zeaxanthin	Cress leaf, Swiss chard, okra, beet greens.	May prevent macular degeneration. Blocks peroxide free radicals.

CAROTENOID-ENHANCED VEGETABLES

By 2002 many vegetables will have their genes altered to force the vegetables to produce a higher level of carotenoids, which are at the forefront of present day scientific investigations regarding cancer prevention. By increasing the carotenoid levels the vegetables will also be more resistant to browning from exposure to the air.

CO-ENZYME Q10 (UBIQUINONE)

Ubiquinone10 is not a vitamin and can be produced by the body from two proteins: tyrosine and mevalonate. Ubiquinone10 is necessary for the cell to produce energy and has proved to be an active antioxidant in reducing free radical production. A number of factors may reduce the available Ubiquinone10 in the body causing lower energy levels. Dietary sources of the nutrients needed to produce Ubiquinone10 are lean meats, nuts, vegetables, and grains

Studies have shown that if levels of Ubiquinone10 are low (below 25% of normal levels) cells cannot produce enough energy to live and cells will start to die until the level increases. The elderly, malnourished, and chronically ill have lower levels of Ubiquinone10 and may need to be supplemented. However, if a sufficient supply is always available energy levels will be maintained.

Ubiquinone10 may also be active in keeping the immune system healthy and at optimum efficiency.

SHARK CARTILAGE

Studies are continuing in all major countries regarding the use of shark cartilage and the prevention or treatment of cancer. Most studies are finding that there is an ingredient that seems to reduce the growth of tumors. The following results have been taken from a small study of only 21 patients and should be viewed in that context:

- 61%   had a reduction in tumor size
- 87%   stated that they had improved their quality of life
- 100%   of prostate cancer patients had a lower PSA level

When claims are made it is best to obtain a copy of the study and review it before taking this or any new product for an extended period of time.

DHEA (dehydroepiandrosterone)

Naturally occurring hormone which may enhance the efficiency of the immune system. It is normally produced by the adrenal gland and is a component of a number of hormones, such as: testosterone, progesterone, estrogen, and corticosterone.

As we age the blood levels of DHEA decline and studies are being done to determine if this decline may speed up the aging process. It has been used successfully to increase libido in persons that have experienced a lowering of their sex drive as related to aging. Many of the degenerative effects of aging may be slowed with the supplementation of this as we age.

Studies, however, are not conclusive at this time to actually prescribe a dosage that would be beneficial for a specific problem. DHEA has been banned by the government until more studies are done. However, herbal products are being sold that companies claim to be the precursor of DHEA. These herbal products are for the most part derived from the Mexican Yam (Dioscorea villosa) roots. Also called diosgenin and can be converted to DHEA in the body.

High dosages when given to rats have caused liver damage.

ANTIOXIDANT ENZYMES

Superoxide Dismutase (SOD)

One of the first lines of defense the body has from free radicals is from a substance called SOD. SOD is a natural antioxidant that keeps the free radicals under control and eliminates them. SOD always has a partner called "catalase" which helps carry away some of the debris when SOD reacts with a free radical. The most dangerous element of the debris is hydrogen peroxide, which if left alone will create additional more destructive free radicals.

This partnership is one of the most effective free radical eliminators in our bodies. A deficiency of SOD can reduce the body's effectiveness in fighting free radicals and increases the risk and severity of a number of diseases such as arthritis, bursitis, and gout.

Glutathione Peroxidase (GP)

The main constituents of this antioxidant enzyme is the amino acid glutathione and the mineral selenium. One of selenium's main functions in the body is to become a component of the glutathione peroxidase enzyme.

The key role of GP in the body is to protect the lipids in the cell walls from being destroyed by a group of free radicals known as lipid peroxides. Studies are being done to determine the significance of the cell damage by peroxides (when adequate GP is not present) in relation to diseases such as: heart disease, premature aging, cancer, liver and pancreas damage, and skin disorders.

Methionine Reductase (MR)

This antioxidant enzyme has been effective in neutralizing another free radical called a hydroxyl radical. These are formed by the reactions involving heavy metals and other free radicals. Hydroxy radicals are also formed by the exposure of the body to x-rays and radiation. MR plays a significant role in the destruction and neutralization of these free radicals, especially the ones formed by athletes or during strenuous exercise periods.

Hydroxy radicals are a by-product of fat metabolism, which occurs after the depletion of our carbohydrate stores. An athlete that can keep a high level of MR during a strenuous exercise period or sport may be able to improve their performance.

CHLORELLA

Chlorella is derived from freshwater algae and is one of the newest green algae products. It has 50 times the chlorophyll content of alfalfa and scientists estimate it has survived for approximately 2.5 billion years. Studies have concluded that the longevity of chlorella is due to the strength of its hard cell wall and unique DNA repair mechanism.

Only recently has science discovered a method of breaking down the hard cell wall and be able to produce it as a health food. At present, chlorella is the fastest-selling health food product in Japan and is used as both a dietary supplement and for medicinal purposes. Chlorella has a high protein content, approximately 60% compared to soybean's 30% making it an excellent non-meat protein source.

Chlorella contains over 20 vitamins and minerals and is an excellent source of vitamin B12, especially for vegetarians. Chlorella is far superior than spirulina in all categories. Studies are surfacing showing that chlorophyll has been related to improved metabolism, tissue growth (wound healing), and lowering cholesterol levels. Additional studies are ongoing relating to cancer prevention since chlorella may stimulate the immune system to produce macrophages, which kill abnormal cells. At present, all studies regarding cancer and chlorella are all being conducted in Japan.

NEW TEST FOR ANTIOXIDANT LEVELS IN FOODS

A new test that is called the Oxygen Radical Absorbance Capacity (ORAC) is available that will determine the level of active antioxidants in a specific food. Certain foods such as prunes and blueberries are being evaluated for their ultra-high level of special antioxidants that may actually slow the aging process. The fruits and vegetables received the highest ORAC scores were:

FRUITS		VEGETABLES	
Prunes	5770	Kale	1770
Raisins	2830	Spinach	1260
Blueberries	2400	Brussels Sprouts	980
Blackberries	2036	Alfalfa Sprouts	930
Strawberries	1540	Broccoli Flowers	890
Raspberries	1220	Beets	840
Plums	949	Red Bell Pepper	710
Oranges	750	Onion	450
Red Grapes & Juice	739	Corn	400

FARMERS WILL BE WORKING PHARMACISTS

Functional foods will be one of the most important areas of food technology in the 21st century. By 2010 almost all foods will be genetically altered, electrically pulsed, nutrient enriched, become nutraceuticals, appear in new types of packaging, and be bacteria-free. The scientific food alteration revolution is on with science claiming its all for the better. The more educated the consumer becomes, the more they will understand the importance of functional foods. The changes in food should increase life expectancy by at least 25 years by 2015.

JAPANESE PRODUCING DIGESTIVE FUNCTIONAL FOOD

The Japanese are the first to jump on the bandwagon and produce a complete category of food related to a healthy digestive tract, stressing regularity. Their foods sold for this purpose contain mild laxatives and intestinal cleansers such as inulin, oligofructosaccharide and acidophilus. The foods are becoming extremely popular.

MANIPULATING ALGAE, YEAST, AND FUNGI

Algae, yeast, and fungi are fast growing and easy to alter so that they will collect a variety of nutrients and carry them to a variety of foods. They will concentrate certain nutrients and act as a delivery vehicle to add these nutrients into foods, thus increasing the foods nutrient value. Algae is also being use to boost crop yields by altering a gene that allows more efficient use of nitrogen by the plants.

GBL WARNING FROM FDA

Gamma butyrolactone (GBL) is a solvent that may be found in dietary supplements to improve sleep, enhance sexual performance and increase energy levels. GBL can be converted into GHB, a very potent drug in the body. Over 100 cases have been reported that include problems such as seizures, coma and even death. All supplements were recalled in 1999 but a few companies are still selling the product.

SOY TO FIGHT HEART DISEASE

Soybeans are becoming increasingly popular as a health food. They have high levels of a number of important nutrients, especially isoflavones. A new tasty product will be available in major supermarkets called "Neatloaf." In the very near future a breakfast cereal will be available that will also contain soy. The University of Illinois is working on a new type of extrusion process that will allow the isoflavones in soy to be more readily available. The cereals should be at the supermarkets by late 2000. Studies are also proving that consuming soy can lower cholesterol blood levels.

DRINK BLUEBERRY JUICE FOR EYE STRAIN

The Japanese have developed a blueberry juice that contains high levels of anthocyanin. This compound has been related to overall eye and retina health, especially for people who spend long hours in front of a computer screen. Blueberries are one of the best sources and the Japanese are producing a complete line of products related to increasing blueberry consumption among office workers.

NEW CHEWABLE CALCIUM

A new supplement will soon be available that will provide your daily requirement of calcium in a chewable form. The new product will be chocolate or coffee flavored and will be sold in a 12-pack as well as a 60-count package. The packages resemble a candy package and chewing two of the treats will supply you with your calcium.

CANDY WITH A BUZZ

A new candy that will provide you with a caffeine "buzz" will be available within a few months. Five pieces of the taffy-like concoction will supply you with the equivalent amount of caffeine to equal one cup of regular coffee. The candy will be sold in four flavors: vanilla, espresso, mocha and chocolate.

CHICKEN SOUP MAY REALLY WORK

A new line of prescription soups will be arriving at your local supermarket by early 2000. The soups will be produced by Hain's Kitchen and will contain specific herbs that are related historically to different illnesses, such as colds and osteoporosis. The FDA still has to approve the wording on the labels before the products can be released.

COMMON FRUITS WITH THE MOST VITAMIN C

1. Strawberries
2. Oranges
3. Kiwi
4. Lychees
5. Canteloupe
6. Mangoes
7. Gooseberries
8. Grapefruit
9. Raspberries
10. Pineapple

COMMON VEGETABLES WITH THE MOST BETA-CAROTENE

1. Carrots
2. Sweet Potatoes
3. Spinach
4. Pumpkin
5. Jalapeno Peppers
6. Okra

OUTSTANDING NEW PRODUCT FOR WEIGHT CONTROL

The new product is "Healthy Pleasures." It is a dairy-type drink that is sold as a shake and is 99% fat free. It is the first dairy-based, shelf-stable nutrition shake that has ever been sold in a wide-mouthed resealable glass bottle. It is fortified with 20 vitamins and minerals. It is being sold not only as a diet control drink, but a health drink as well.

NEW APPETITE SUPPRESSANT

A British drug firm; the Scotia Holdings Plc, has developed a new appetite suppressant called "Olibra." The product will be placed into General Mills products in the United States, Canada, and Mexico. The suppressant will probably be placed into yogurt and a number of desserts.

LIST OF SUPPLEMENTS IN ORDER OF IMPORTANCE TO THE PUBLIC

1. Antioxidants	11. Isoflavones
2. Calcium	12. Vitamin A
3. Vitamin E	13. Green Tea Extract
4. Dietary Fiber	14. Ginko Biloba
5. Vitamin C	15. High Oleic Fats
6. Folic Acid	16. Oligosaccharides
7. Omega-3 Fatty Acids	17. Yogurt Cultures
8. Ginseng	18. Fish Oils
9. Garlic	19. Chromium Picolinate
10. Beta-Carotene	20. Choline

Source: Prepared Foods R&D Investment Survey 1999

NEW WEIGHT CONTROL ACID

Studies now show that conjugated linoleic acid (CLA) may be the answer to weight control in some individuals. The mice that were fed the CLA reduced their body fat by about 25% without a major change in their dietary habits. CLA is also being investigated for its relationship to reducing the incidence in cancer among higher risk people. Norway is conducting studies and results should be more accurate by early 2000. CLA is found in higher concentrations in animal products such as fresh ground beef, lamb, Colby cheese, Mozzarella cheese, Ricotta cheese, milk, plain yogurt, cottage cheese and sour cream.

A VERY FINE NEW DIET DRINK

VeryFine, Inc. will be marketing a new diet juice drink that will use sucralose instead of aspartame (Equal). Sucralose is made from sugar and is calorie-free. The drinks will be marketed nationally and may not appear in all stores until early 2000. The products will have very few calories and excellent taste.

THE CURE FOR SEA SICKNESS

A new beverage claims to have the answer to seasickness. If you drink a can of Sailor's Ginger Delight you will not be seasick. Ginger has been used for hundreds of years to alleviate seasickness and does work when taking the capsules. If their claims are true this is an easy way to cure a miserable problem. The drink is a sparkling beverage that has a taste of tropical passion fruit and ginger. It contains no artificial flavors, caffeine or sodium and gets very high marks in the taste category.

NEW TEST FOR MINERAL CONTENT

There is a new piece of equipment available to the general public that will evaluate the mineral content of solid foods and liquids. The Meridian Liquid & Food Tester can be placed in any food or liquid and will let you know the extent of mineral content of that food. The unit sells for $79.95 and further information can be obtained by calling (313) 272-3045.

VITAMIN F

Vitamin F is actually an essential fatty acid that is derived from vegetable oils. The vitamin is being studied in relation to a number of skin disorders, prostate problems, and asthma.

SPRINKLE ON SUPPLEMENTS COMING SOON

Supplements will soon be available in single pack, sprinkle on vitamins and minerals that can be placed on foods as a type of seasoning. They will also be available in shakers that can be used when cooking or preferably after the cooking is completed to retain more nutrients that might be affected by heat or hot foods.

CHOCOLATE BARS TO FIGHT ARTERY DISEASES

The Japanese have added Polyphenol, which is normally found in red wine and to a small degree chocolate, to chocolate bars. Polyphenol is the compound that was isolated from red wine after it was found that drinking red wine may be the reason the French do not have as high a rate of cardiovascular disease as the Americans. In another related study regarding chocolate and heart disease by the University of California at Davis, the same results were obtained pointing to similar flavenoids.

LYCOPENE SPIKED DRINKS

Many drinks are now being supplemented with the antioxidant, lycopene, which is found in high levels in tomatoes and tomato products.

SALES WILL BE IN BILLIONS BY 2003

Nutraceutical sales, which include all products that have had nutrients added to them, will reach $22.1 billion by 2003. The products will range anywhere from soft drinks to chewing gum to frozen meals. Almost every food company in the world is gearing up for a big sales push of these new functional foods.

FORTIFIED FOODS MAY REPLACE MANY SUPPLEMENTS

Predictions by a number of market research groups believe that by 2005-2010 functional foods will replace many present day supplements. Surveys taken show that the public would prefer to have their supplements in their foods than take a pill if they have a choice.

LIPTON TO MARKET ANTI-CHOLESTEROL SPREAD

Early in 2002 your market should be selling a new functional food that is formulated to promote healthy cholesterol levels. The new food has been approved by the FDA and contains vegetable oil sterol esters. The new product will be called "Take Control" and is presently being test marketed in the Chicago area markets. Plant sterols are all-natural and work with the digestive system in reducing the absorption of cholesterol. The product will be sold in a 10-ounce tub and packages that contain 16 individual portions.

COOKIES THAT WILL BE COLON-FRIENDLY

Watch for a new cookie that will be colon-friendly. The cookie will be called "Pro-Crunch" and will contain "inulin." Inulin has the ability to assist the body in the production of friendly bacteria, which are beneficial to the health of the colon. Next time the doctor prescribes an antibiotic, which may kill the "good bacteria" he may tell you have a few cookies with your medicine.

NEW ATHLETES PRODUCT

Research reports are just starting to surface regarding the simple sugar "ribose." Ribose is an important component of DNA and RNA and important in the production of energy and rebuilding muscle cells. The sugar may be an important supplement in aiding athletes in rejuvenating their energy levels after strenuous workouts or sports activity.

LIQUID NUTRITIONAL PRODUCTS

DIET DRINKS

The liquid and powder diet drinks on the market are for the most part formulated with milk, soy, or grain derivative as the main ingredient. Many are now using glucomannan, an appetite suppressant in their products, herbs, tea extracts, enzymes, vitamins, minerals, and free amino acids. Some of the more popular products will be mentioned and some of their claims. While most of the products are high quality products that contain good ingredients, I have not found any product after practicing weight control for 23 years that was effective for any length of time without a good structured program of exercise, nutrition education, stress management, and behavior modification.

BE TRIM TOO

Sells a concentrated product that is in liquid form and just a few drops are placed in a glass of water or juice. The ingredients are herbs, vitamins, minerals, and enzymes. They also sell a product that claims to assist the body in metabolizing stored body fat while you sleep that contains L-carnitine, amino acids, green tea, atractylodes extract, B vitamins, choline, and chromium picolinate.

CRAVE CURE

This drink is being sold as a diet drink and a general nutrition drink since it contains numerous vitamins, minerals, grain derivatives, amino acids, and an appetite suppressant. The drink is recommended for breakfast or lunch, then eat a sensible dinner. The drink is also referred to as an energy drink. It is a nutritionally sound drink and if it were a component of a structured weight program would get my nod.

FORM YOU 3

This is a meal replacement drink that is sold in a variety of flavors and contains soy protein isolate, folic acid, 25 additional vitamins and minerals, is low-fat and lactose free. It is sold in packets and can be mixed with water or juice.

MAXIMUM FAT BURNER LIQUID ENERGY

This is a highly concentrated liquid fat burner product that contains L-carnitine, choline, inositol, vitamin B6, 10 grams of carbohydrate, and chromium picolinate.

PERFECT SUPER RIPPED

This is one of a number of beverages sold all using the Perfect brand name. The company claims that there are many "fake fat burning drinks" on the market and is quick to display their own formulation as the best and one of the "real" ones. The drink contains 3mg of ephedra from Ma Huang (low potency stimulant), 2mg of chitosan (fat absorber), 1mg of white willow bark, and 250mg of L-carnitine and 100 mg of caffeine. Chiton is usually derived from the exoskeleton of shellfish and there is not one double-blind study that I am aware of that relates the compound to increasing fat metabolism in humans.

SLIM-SLIM

One of their products is called Total Toddy and is one of their weight management products, Total Toddy contains 7 major minerals, up to 65 trace minerals in liquid bio-electrical organic form from plants, 16 vitamins, 19 amino acids and phytonutrients from vegetables and fruits. The company claims that the product is 98% absorbable. Other products include: Ultra Body Toddy, a liquid dietary supplement, and Slim-Slim Metabolic Fuel.

LIQUID L-CARNITINE 1000

Sold as a "high potency fast absorbing" source of L-carnitine. It is composed of L-carnitine, filtered water, vegetable glycerine, and B vitamins to assist in the absorption of the L-carnitine.

COLLOIDAL MINERALS

A colloid is a substance that is able to retain its identity when placed into a liquid and stay in suspension without falling to the bottom of the bottle. They are extremely small particles and easily absorbed into the cells. Quality colloidal products are produced from special ancient soils, called "humic shale." The minerals are extracted and processed, then separated into the minerals that are the most beneficial to human health, minerals for the most part that we are deficient in.

Colloidal minerals can be 98% absorbed and claims are made that they will eliminate "nutritional fatigue" in most individuals. They also tend to be easily transported to the cells for easy utilization. Claims are also being made that colloidal minerals provide natural cleansing and detoxifying for the body.

HI HO SILVER, COLLOIDAL THAT IS

Silver is now being sold in liquid form since studies show that we may be deficient due to lack of this trace mineral in the soil. A number of farms are now replacing silver, which is being added to the fertilizers. While it is only present in the body in small amounts, it may be useful in the health of a number of body functions. Products should only be sold with concentrations of 10 parts per million or less to be on the safe side.

LIQUID VITAMINS

One of the most common questions asked of nutritionists is whether it is best to obtain your vitamins from solid foods or liquids. The answer is that as long as your digestive system is functioning normally it really doesn't make any difference, which one you get your vitamins from. Vitamins are vitamins and the body will metabolize both in the same manner. Many companies claim that liquid vitamins are more easily absorbed, however, while this is true, there is also more risk of the liquid vitamins being destroyed by stomach enzymes and acids.

SQUIRT YOUR VITAMINS

The latest method of taking your daily dose of vitamins is a spray mist, which is sprayed under the tongue and has higher absorption rate than many tablet vitamin products. The companies selling the product claims that the absorption rate is as high as 90% while tablets may only provide a 10% absorption rate.

TODDIES

Most toddy products sold contain vitamins in liquid form and a number of herbs that are related to blood cleansing and are frequently associated with claims of recuperative benefits. Some toddy products incorporate food grade hydrogen peroxide into their drinks as well as colloidal minerals. The number of different toddy products sold is increasing every day since the public seems to prefer a flavored drink instead of taking a tablet.

HAVE A SHOT OF COD LIVER OIL

Cod liver oil is a good source of omega-3 fatty acids and a lot less expensive than the omega-3 nutritional supplements being sold. However, you may want to flavor it a bit and thin it out somewhat. On second thought, keep taking the ampoules.

LIQUID NUTRITIONAL INFORMATION

CALCIUM CHECK

If you are curious whether your calcium supplement is of a good quality, try placing a tablet in vinegar. If the tablet dissolves completely within 6-8 minutes, it is a good quality product. The government allows 15-30 minutes for vitamins.

THE GREEN LIQUID

Chlorophyll is not available in liquid form as a nutritional supplement. Companies that market the product state that the product can be taken as a blood cleanser, will increase the production of hemoglobin, strengthen cells, improve immune system response, and as an overall body deodorizer.

CAN YOU POWER UP WITH LIQUID CREATINE?

The products that are sold are actually creatine monohydrate and are being marketed as the "most effective sports supplement ever sold." Creatine, is reported to allow the body to work harder and longer without tiring and is used by body builders worldwide and many sports teams. It is not a steroid and from all indications to date, the chemical is safe. The liquid form tends to be effective in a shorter period of time and is recommended for those in a hurry for the effects to kick in.

HOW STABLE ARE VITAMINS IN BEVERAGES?

Vitamin A: May be damaged by oxygen, heat, metal ions, and ultraviolet light. Health drinks that add vitamin A should have a warning regarding these factors. The bottles should be a dark-color not a clear container.

Vitamin B1: Can be damaged at a pH of 6 or over, which means that the more basic the liquid, the more damage will be done. Exposure to heat and oxygen will also take their toll.

Vitamin B2: Can easily be damaged by light in liquids but not in dry products. Bases will also damage B2 since they prefer a somewhat acid environment.

Niacin: A very stable vitamin, which is almost impossible to destroy.

Vitamin B6: Usually very stable in most beverages.

Vitamin B12: Can be destroyed by sunlight and prefers a pH of 4-5.

Pantothenic Acid: May be destroyed in an acidic environment.

Vitamin E: Usually stable, unless the beverage is basic in nature.

Vitamin C: Easily destroyed by oxidation and the potency is reduced if it comes into contact with iron or copper. Heat will also adversely affect vitamin C.

Vitamin D: Can be damaged by light, heat, and oxygen.

SUPER FOODS

A number of drinks are now calling themselves "super foods." These drinks are led by the "Naked" brand of beverages and contain a variety of fruit juices mixed with everything from royal jelly to spirulina to spinach to broccoli. If you don't want pure juice, this is one of the better substitutes.

SPORTS DRINKS

Current literature regarding sports drinks all come to the same conclusion that unless you are performing a strenuous, sports activity or exercising for more than one hour there is no need for a special drink other than water. Sports drinks may be beneficial under certain conditions. Mixing one quart of orange juice with one quart of water, then adding $1\frac{1}{2}$ teaspoons of salt may make a homemade drink.

Most of these drinks are sold to body builders and athletes, which is the target market. The majority of the drinks are healthy, however, it is questionable how effective these drinks really are since there are few studies, if any good double-blind studies to support the claims. The drinks are harmless and do supply a number of nutrients that may replace ones that are depleted through strenuous exercise or sports activities.

ALOE VERA DRINK

This is a natural health/sports drink that is composed of Aloe Vera (no Aloin), vitamins, minerals, and amino acids.

POWERADE®

This drink claims to have more electrolytes and carbohydrate content than Gatorade. It is manufactured by the Coca-Cola Company who I am sure will take their name off this product if it is still on the market when this book is printed. The drink looks like green water and is supposed to be a lemon-lime drink, but has almost no flavor at all.

PRO COMPLEX ® "THE DRINK"

Produced for athletes and contains 40 grams of whey protein isolate and 2 grams of carbohydrate. Claims are made that you will get a faster recovery and "pack on lean muscle" with this drink.

PRO-LIFE®

The drink is a combination of lemon, lime, and orange juice and a large number of micronutrients. It also includes 5 grams of soluble fiber. The taste is excellent and is being sold as a sports/health drink.

GATORADE®

Gatorade is now owned by the Quaker Oats Company. The University of Florida developed Gatorade in 1965 for the Florida Gators, football team. The formula is supposed to help prevent dehydration and replace electrolytes (especially sodium) and supply carbohydrates. Supplying these needed nutrients during strenuous exercise periods has proved to be only somewhat beneficial. Gatorade is one of better quality, good tasting drinks in this category.

Gatorade in 2001 sold $219 million of its new "Frost" line of drinks, which included; Whitewater, Splash, and Alpine Snow.

ULTIMATE ORANGE®

Has been sold as a sports drink since 1982. Ultimate Orange is recommended to be consumed before and after training to increase energy supplies, pre-exercise and to renew energy supplies, post exercise. It is mixed with water and contains Ma Huang, guarana seed, green tea, ginseng, bioflavenoids, omega-3-fatty acids Xylitol, natural flavors, lecithin, cellulose gum and food coloring. One of the better sports drinks.

RATINGS OF SPORTS DRINKS:

The following sports drinks were rated on the number of calories in 8 ounces, carbohydrate content, level of sodium and potassium, cost per container and cost per serving.

10-K
All Sport
All Sport Lite
Exceed (liquid and powder)
Gatorade (liquid and powder)
Gatorade Lite
Hydra Fuel (liquid and powder)
Nautilus Plus
Powerade
Snapple Snap-Up

Source: Consumers Report Magazine

ENERGY DRINKS AND GELS

Since it is only possible to review a limited number of energy drinks, I have chosen some of the more popular ones on the market. Many of these beverages use guarana and caffeine in combination to produce temporary mood elevation and a state of being wide awake. People tend to confuse the state of not being tired with increased energy levels, which is really not the case. High caffeine levels in these drinks will cause an addiction similar to coffee addiction in many susceptible individuals if they consume enough of the product on a regular basis.

ENERGY GELS

These are small packets of very highly concentrated carbohydrates that claim to replace glycogen stores, the body's source of energy. Each packet contains 25 grams of carbohydrates totaling 100 calories. The ingredients consist of a simple sugar usually fructose or dextrose and complex carbohydrates. They do not contain any fiber and most do not contain any protein. The cost is about $1.00 per packet and they will deliver more energy than a power bar. They may help to maintain muscle glycogen (energy storage factor) if taken every 30 minutes with 8 ounces of water.

Consuming high carbohydrate foods just before a strenuous exercise period may accomplish the same as the gel. Gels are recommended for athletes who work out or perform a sport for more than 2 hours.

The gels are not recommended for post exercise recovery when a combination of protein and carbohydrates will re-supply the lost glycogen faster.

GINSENG ENHANCED WATER

A number of companies are now selling ginseng water as an energy enhancing drink. While ginseng has been used to increase energy levels for hundreds of years and normally sold in capsule form. The benefits ginseng that has been diluted with water may not have adequate potency and should be studied further before any claims are made.

NATURAL LIQUID SPRAYS

A number of all natural homeopathic spays are now available through distributors nationwide. These sprays are formulated from a number of all-natural ingredients and homeopathic nutritional extracts. They are sprayed under the tongue (sub-lingual) and therefore can be absorbed and utilized very quickly. There are studies that show the efficacy of these products and more studies should be surfacing in the next year or two that will relate to larger population studies and positive results in a good percentage of the population.

They have no side effects, unlike conventional pharmaceuticals, which make them an excellent alternative form of medicinal product. All products are sold in 2 ounce spray bottles (not aerosol) with an expiration date and a list of all ingredients. These products would make a great natural edition to the family medicine cabinet. The ingredient names are homeopathic tongue twisters, therefore they will not be included.

GENERAL NUTRITIONAL DRINKS

There are a number of drinks on the market and more appearing almost daily. This category includes drinks such as Ensure®, Sustain®, Boost®, and Resource®, etc. They all contain different formulations but for the most part all contain water, sugars, oils, milk or milk derivatives, vitamin and minerals. Some now contain herbs. Sales of Ensure in 2001 were about $336 million out of estimated total sales in the United States of $709 million.

These drinks are not a replacement for a meal but will give you a level of additional nutrition, especially for those who find it difficult to eat properly on certain days or have medical problems that affect their absorption of nutrients in whole foods.

ENSURE™

Ensure™ has 250 calories in an 8 ounce serving, 6.1 grams of fat which amounts to 22% of the total calories, 40 grams of carbohydrate, 8.8 grams of protein and cost about $1.65 per serving. This is one of the better quality drinks.

CHAPTER 18

PETS, INSECTS AND PESKY CRITTERS

VEGGIE-CATS & VEGGIE-DOGS

By the year 2002 your animal may be eating a pure, vegetarian diet and like it. Studies have shown that animals will be healthier and enjoy their food just as much if it is vegetarian.

HAIR SPRAY TO THE RESCUE

To get rid of flies and bees, just spray them with hair spray.

DON'T USE AMMONIA CLEANERS

Never use any cleaner that has ammonia in it to clean a pet stain. The smell of ammonia will make your pet want to use the same spot again.

DRAWING THE LINE WHEN IT COMES TO ANTS

Ants will not cross a chalk line. They hate to get their feet in any type of powder. Baby powder works good too. They also stay away from bay leaves, cloves and cucumber peelings.

GETTING BATS OUT OF THE BELFRY & ATTIC

If you place 5-6 boxes of mothballs that contain the chemical "naphthaline" in the attic, it will stop the bats from residing there.

TALK ABOUT INDIGESTION

Sugar ants will never come back if you sprinkle some cayenne pepper in the windowsills. This will give them a stomachache they will never forget. They will also track it back to the nest.

KEEPING OUT RABBITS & DEER

Bloodmeal will keep these animals from your property.

DEER DETERRENT

Mix together: 2 eggs, 2 cups of water, 4 cloves of crushed garlic and 2 teaspoons of Tabasco sauce. Allow the mixture to stand for 2 days then spray with a garden sprayer in all areas of yard area.

VITAMIN C FOR PREGNANT DOGS

If you find your pregnant dog searching the garden for rose petals or citrus fruit peelings, don't get upset, they know what they are doing. Giving your pet a vitamin C supplement 3-4 weeks before they whelp makes the process easier for your pet. Even though animals are still able to produce vitamin C and humans can't, they tend to burn up more than they can produce during this period.

DOG FOOD FACTS

Dog food is always better for your dog than table scraps. Dogs do not have the enzyme in their saliva to pre-digest starches. Dogs need foods that are easily digestible, such as meat products that contain a good level of unsaturated fatty acids. Saturated fats are hard for the dog to digest. The more simple carbohydrates and a good quality fiber found in dog foods are the best and should be part of a quality food. Most dog foods are vitamin enriched providing a good balance of nutrients. Premium dog foods are in almost every case the best food for your dog.

CAT AND DOG STOMACH FACTS

Dogs as we all know will eat certain foods until they gorge themselves. Cats, however, only eat what they need. Their stomach is only the size of about a 50-cent piece so they have to be fussy. It doesn't pay to give cats a big plate of food; they have no place to put it.

GETTING RID OF THE CRAWLEEES

A number of herbs will ward off crawling insects. The most potent are cloves, bay leaves, and sage. Placing any of these herbs in locations where a problem may exist will stop the critters cold and cause them to do an about face and leave the premises. Ants, roaches, and spiders are especially hard to get rid of, however, a few old remedies seem to really work well. If the above herbs don't work, try mixing 2 cups of 20 Mule Team Boraxo with any powdered sweetener in a large container; and sprinkle areas that you know they frequent. Crawling insects will also not cross a fine powder such as baby powder.

NATURAL INSECTICIDE

If you have a problem with any type of flying insect, try keeping a basil plant or two around the house. Keep the plant well, watered from the bottom, this will cause the plant to release additional aroma. Hanging small muslin bags with fresh dried basil will also repel flying insects. Works on anything with wings!

BLACK ANTS: A PROBLEM?

If you place pieces of wormwood in areas around their home, you will never see them again. **However, wormwood can be toxic to children and pets.**

KEEP CATS & DOGS OUT OF THE GARDEN

Place a pop bottle that has been filled with 2 parts ammonia and 1 part of water in the ground near your garden and allow the open top to be just above ground level.

SPIDERS, BEWARE

Place the herb pennyroyal on cotton balls and place anywhere you have a problem.

YOU WON'T NEED THE ROD AND REEL

To get rid of silverfish, try mixing 1 part of molasses in 2 parts of white vinegar. Apply the mixture to cracks and holes where they reside. Treat the baseboards and table legs as well.

OOOOPS

If your dog or cat has an accident use a small amount of white vinegar in a spray bottle to remove the odor. However, try a small area that is out of sight to make sure the carpet is colorfast. Use paper towel first to remove as much of the liquid as possible. A mild solution of hot soapy water should do the trick as well.

ROTTEN EGGS TO THE RESCUE

Keeping deer, antelope, and reindeer away from your garden and trees is a breeze with eggs that have gone bad and float in water. Just break them open (outside of the house) around the area that you want to keep the critters away from. The smell of hydrogen sulfide from rotten eggs is not one of their favorite aromas. Another method is to grate deodorant soap (not the sweet-smelling stuff), place the gratings in small cloth sacs and hang a few sacs on each tree.

FASTER THAN RABBITS

Garbage cans and trash compactors can produce 1,000 or more flies a week unless they are sealed tight. Flies, however, are repelled by oil of lavender. Soak a sponge with the oil and leave it in a saucer, or place the oil on a cotton ball and add it to your garbage the beginning of each week. Other natural fly repellents are oil of cloves and mint sprigs.

NATURAL INSECTICIDE

If you are going to plant in window boxes, try whitewashing them first. This will deter insects and reduce the risk of dry rot.

BUG KILLER

If you place a few drops of liquid detergent in your water that is being used to clean the plant's leaves, it will keep the bugs off and if they go into the soil at night they will die.

FLEA: SUCTION

Fleas; can be eliminated by vacuuming with a high-powered vacuum cleaner (Preferably Electrolux™) with a good sealing bag. Remove the bag and dispose of it immediately after vacuuming.

PROTEIN AND PETS

Both cats and dogs require about 6 times the protein as we do.

THE CABBAGE PATCH SLUG

If you're having problems with slugs eating your flowers, there is a simple solution. Just plant a few cabbage plants in your garden. Slugs go crazy for cabbage plants, try it, it works great.

GETTING RID OF CARPENTER ANTS

Prepare a mixture of $\frac{1}{2}$ cup of molasses, 1 package of dry yeast and $\frac{1}{4}$ cup of granulated sugar. Mix well and spread on a piece of cardboard, then place where you have a problem.

ONE FOR THE SQUIRREL

One of the deadliest mushrooms is the Amanita. Gray squirrels have developed a method of detoxifying the mushroom so that can eat it without being harmed.

ODOR CONTROLLER

Citronella oil candles will rid your home of mosquitoes. The smell is pleasant and not at all offensive. Placing tall gas, lights around the backyard when your having an outdoor event with a few drops of citronella oil added to it, will keep the backyard clear of moths and mosquitoes.

MOSQUITOES WILL FLY AWAY FROM BEAN PLANT

If you want an easy solution to ridding your home and garden of mosquitoes, just purchase some castor seeds and grow a few plants. The castor bean plants will grow like a weed and will repel mosquitoes.

MOTH TRAPPER

Moths can be trapped by mixing 1 part of molasses with 2 parts of white vinegar and placing the mixture in a bright yellow container.

KEEPING YOUR DOG HOT

If you want to keep a hot dog hot until lunchtime, try placing it into a thermos filled with a hot beverage wrapped in plastic wrap or in a baggie.

PHEWWW

Next time you change the litter box, try adding a small layer of baking soda on the bottom to absorb odors. A small amount of baking soda applied to your armpits can replace your deodorant.

NUTRAPET

Vitamins and minerals are very important to your pet's health. Save the water from boiled vegetables or liquid from a crock-pot and mix it with your animal's food for additional nutrients.

TRAPPER TOAD

Finding a toad in your garden is really good luck. One lonely toad will feast on over 100 slugs, cutworms, grubs, caterpillar, and assorted beetle larvae. If the toad is in top form it can consume over 10,000 invaders in one season.

SNAIL: ZAPPER

Place stale cheap beer in a shallow container just below ground level. Snails are attracted to beer (why I don't know) the beer, however, tends to have a diuretic effect, causing the snail to lose excess liquids in a short period of time and die.

RODENT REPELLER #1

Moles, squirrels, gophers, rats, and mice hate the aroma of peppermint. If you plant mint around your home chances are you will never see one for any length of time. If you place a small amount of oil of peppermint on a cotton ball and drop it down a gopher hole you will never see the varmint again.

HUNTING LICENSE NEEDED TO CATCH MICE

In Cleveland, Ohio there is still an old, old law on the books that prohibits catching mice without a hunting license.

RODENT REPELLER #2

Another method of getting rid of unwanted rodents and related animals is to place a few drops of "Nepeta" or catnip oil on a cotton ball and place it anywhere the problem exists.

HERE, KITTY, KITTY

To remove a grease stain from your concrete driveway, try rubbing kitty litter into the stain and allow tit o stand for 1-2 hours before sweeping it up. Don't let the cat out.

WHERE DID FIDO GO?

To ward off fleas from a pet's sleeping area, try sprinkling a few drops of oil of lavender in the area. Fleas hate oil of lavender, hopefully your dog won't.

POOR BAMBI

Hanging small pieces of a deodorant bar soap on trees will keep the deer away. Works excellent on fruit trees! Also, try a piece of your clothing; they don't like the smell of humans.

TAKE TWO AND SEE ME IN THE MORNING

Chigger bites respond to a thick paste of a few aspirin tablets with water. Should ease the pain and itching.

CARPENTER ANTS & TERMITES A PROBLEM, FEED THEM CAT FOOD

It's not necessary to poison your pets and drive the family out of the house for a week to get rid of carpenter ants. Just mix up a batch of 4 ounces of cherry or grape jelly in 3 tablespoons of canned cat food and 1 tablespoon of boric acid. Place small amounts of the batch in any location that ants frequent. The ant who finds the food will take it to their leader (queen) and the colony will be eliminated. A termite can live up to the ripe old age of 50.

GENERAL INSECT BITES

Place 2 Alka-Seltzer® tablets in a glass of water and allow to dissolve. Dip a cloth into the water and hold the cloth on the bite for about 15 minutes.

FRUIT FLY KILLER

If fruit flies are a problem, just mix up a batch of the following and leave it in a shallow container. Mix ½ quart of tap water with 2 Tbsp of sugar, 2 Tbsp of white vinegar and 5 drop of liquid soap.

SLIPPING AND SLIDING

If you place a border of petroleum jelly (Vaseline) around a plant it should keep the ants away. Also, placing it on the stem of plants will stop most insects including ants from crawling up the plant.

WORRIED ABOUT MOTH EGGS IN YOUR WOOLENS?

All you have to do is place your woolens in a plastic bag and leave it in the freezer for at least 24 hours to kill the eggs. When you do store the garments, try and place them in as airtight a bag as possible.

WEEVIL ELIMINATOR

Weevils tend to take up residency in dried beans and most grains. If you place a dried chili pepper in with your grains you will never find another weevil and it will not affect the grain or beans.

A SPOT OF TEA, WITH A DASH OF AMMONIA

If you want to keep bugs off your indoor plants, try spraying the plants with a solution of 10 parts weak tea and 1-part ammonia. Keep out of reach of children.

KITTY LITTER SMELLS

If you mix ½ cup of baby powder in with the kitty litter it will eliminate the odor between changes.

GONE WITH THE FLEAS

To rid your pet of fleas, cut a strip of cloth about an inch larger than the size of your pets neck. Fold it over so that there is an opening in the center and sew one end shut as well as placing a seam down the strip. Use a funnel to fill the opening with a combination of 50/50 rosemary and oregano, then sew or tape a piece of Velcro to close the open end and attach to pet using the Velcro closure.

ROACHES HATE BORIC ACID

Almost anything that contains grain or sugar can be mixed with boric acid and sprinkled in crevices or cracks where they hang out. This is an effective killer and will not work too fast. That will give them time to get home and may be bring a doggie bag with them for the family.
Keep this concoction out of the reach of children and pets.

ROACHES LOVE ALCOHOLIC BEVERAGES

A good way to rid your home of roaches is to give them one of their favorite drinks: alcohol. A shallow dish placed wherever a problem exists filled with any type of cheap alcoholic beverage, especially wine, should eliminate the roaches.

AH CHOO

One of the more effective methods of animal control is to place small amounts of red pepper around your garden, trees, etc. Plants that are toxic to animals such as oleander need to be sprinkled with pepper.

DON'T MAKE YOURSELF ATTRACTIVE TO BUGS

A variety of different bugs are attracted to different colored clothing. If you wear blue, thrips will follow you around. Whiteflies love the color yellow. A basic brown or khaki color doesn't seem to draw flies or bugs.

SHINE ON, SHINE ON.....

Most animals are usually afraid of anything bright and shiny. Try hanging strips of foil on trees or shrubs.

MOSQUITOES SMARTER THAN ZAPPERS

Studies have proven that electric bug zappers have no effect on mosquitoes. They seem to have a special sense that keeps then away from electronic magnetic fields. Citronella lamps will do the trick.

CASTOR BEANS FIGHT MOSQUITOES

To keep mosquitoes out of the house, just purchase some castor bean seeds from your nursery and keep a few plants around the house. Mosquitoes will never come near a castor bean plant. The plant will give off enough aroma to keep them out of the house.

MOSQUITO REPELLANT

To keep mosquitoes from biting you, just mix 4 parts of glycerin with 4 parts of isopropyl alcohol and rub on your skin. Another repellant can be made by mixing oil of citronella with Vaseline.

GETTING RID OF MOTHS

To make moth, repellant paper, just mix together 4 parts of naphthalene and 8 parts of paraffin wax. Melt together and paint on paper while it is still warm.

USING WRIGLEY'S FOR WRIGGLERS

Mealworms will avoid your grain products (macaroni, spaghetti, etc.) if you keep a wrapped slice of spearmint gum near the products. They don't like spearmint but are attracted to Juicy Fruit.

TRAPPING MICE WITH PEANUT BUTTER

Mice love the flavor of peanut butter even more than cheese. If you're having problems trapping them with cheese, try some peanut butter.

KEEP FLEAS OFF DOGS

Fleas do not like sage. Crush up as close to a powder as you can and rub it on the pets skin, allow to remain for 20 minutes or until the dog is tired of sitting still, then brush or vacuum off.

SQUIRREL DETERRENT

If squirrels and chipmunks are your problem, just sprinkle a small amount of kitty litter around your plants. The critters will think that there is a cat around. This will only work if there are no cats around to use the litter.

CHAPTER 19

STAINS BEGONE

GENERAL RULES TO REMOVE STAINS

Never wash any fabric before attempting to remove the stain, Washing in a detergent may actually set the stain and make it impossible to remove later.

Stains on washable fabrics should be treated as soon as possible. Remember, fresh stains will come out more easily than old ones. Non-washable items that normally go to the cleaners should be taken to the cleaners as soon as possible. Identify the stain for the dry cleaner. If you know what the stain is be sure and tell them.

LIGHTS ON

When trying to remove stains at home, make sure you do it on a clean, well-lighted work surface. Always use fresh clean rags or a towel.

RUST REMOVAL

Rust stains can be removed by wetting the areas with lemon juice, then sprinkle with a small amount of salt and allow to sit in direct sunlight for 30-45 minutes.

CLEANING STUFFED ANIMALS

The stuffed animal should be placed into a brown paper bag, add cornmeal and shake the bag vigorously for about 1-2 minutes. Brush the cornmeal off with a soft-bristled brush. The cornmeal will absorb oils and even grease.

ELIMINATE SHOWER DOOR SOAP SCUM

Clean the door with a sheet of dampened fabric softener.

STOP SHOE ODORS

Place a sheet of fabric softener in the sneakers or shoes to eliminate odors.

THAT BURNING SENSATION

A scorch can be removed by rubbing a raw onion on the scorched area and allowing the onion juice to soak in thoroughly for at least 2-3 hours before washing.

MAKE SURE IT'S CHILLED

Blood stains may be cleaned with club soda.

A SHINING EXAMPLE

To shine chrome fixture, try rubbing them with newspaper while they are still damp. Baby oil and a soft cloth works well. Aluminum foil will also do the job.

A WORD TO THE WISE

If you are going to use a commercial stain removal substance, be sure and follow directions carefully.

OXYGEN BLEACH Vs. CHLORINE BLEACH

Chlorine bleach is a strong chemical that will kill mildew and may remove colors from fabrics. May be used in washer after wash cycle has run for 5 minutes with colorfast garments. Oxygen bleach is color-safe bleach and can be added to the wash cycle the same time the detergent is added.

VINEGAR DOES WONDERS FOR WHITES

Keep a spray bottle with 50% white vinegar and 50% water handy and spray new whites before placing them into the washer to keep them white.

TESTING, ONE, TWO

Always test a stain remover on an area of the fabric that will not show to be sure of the colorfastness of the fabric. Allow the product to stand on the area for at least 3-5 minutes before rinsing off. If there are any changes in the fabric color, do not use.

HIDE THAT SPOT

When treating a spot, it should be placed face down on paper towel, then apply the stain remover to the underside of the garment, allowing the stain to be forced to the surface and not back through the fabric. The paper towel should be replaced a number of times if it is a tough stain to remove.

WHERE ART THOU COLOR

If you are going to use a bleach product, never use it on a colored garment. It is necessary to bleach the whole garment to avoid uneven color removal. If there is a change in color it will at least be uniform.

NICOTINE STAIN

To remove a nicotine stain on an ashtray, just rub the area with heated salt.

WHITENING TRICK

Place 4-5 lemon slices in a pot of boiling water, add garment and allow it to soak for 40-50 minutes before placing the garment into the washer.

RESIDUES: BEGONE

As soon as the stain is removed, launder immediately with your favorite laundry detergent. This will also remove the residues from the stain remover.

STAIN REMOVAL PRODUCTS

Prompt treatment is the key to stain removal, and it would be wise to have the supplies on hand at all times. The following is a list of some of the more common ingredients needed for most stain removal, however, more natural stain and general cleaning preparations are recommended.

BLEACHES
Chlorine bleach
Fabric color remover
Non-chlorine, all fabric, bleach

MISCELLANEOUS REMOVERS
Ammonia
Rust stain remover
White vinegar

DETERGENTS
Enzyme detergent
Enzyme presoaker
Liquid detergent

SOLVENTS
Dry cleaner spot remover
Nail polish remover
Rubbing alcohol
Turpentine

SOAPS
Laundry detergent
White bar soap

SUPPLIES
Clean white cloths
Paper towels

Any of the above products that cannot be found at the supermarket will be found at any drug store.

CAUTION:

Some stain removal materials are inflammable, while others are poison or toxic. Store them safely and use with care.

CHEMICAL ALERT

Keep stain removal supplies out of reach of children. They should be stored in closed containers with childproof lids and in a cool, dry location away from any food products.

SMELLS NICE TOO

Lemon extract will remove black scuff, marks from shoes and luggage.

HARD ONE TO GET OUT

Stains from ballpoint pens can be removed with hair spray or milk.

READING THE WRITING

Read the labels on cleaning products and follow directions. Heed all label warnings and always try to store them in their original containers.

CONTAINER SMARTS

Empty and wash all containers immediately after using them. It is best to store stain removal supplies in glass or unchipped porcelain containers. Solvents will ruin plastic containers. Rusty containers should never be used

Be careful never allow chemicals near your face and especially your eyes. Wash any spilled chemicals off your hands as soon as possible. .

WEAR A GAS MASK

Use chemicals that give off vapors in a well, ventilated location, preferably outside. Try not to breathe the vapors.

POOOOF

Never use a solvent near an open fire or an electrical outlet.

YUM, YUM, FABRIC

Never add solvents directly into the washing machine. Always allow a solvent-treated fabric dry before washing or placing it into the dryer.

A WITCHES BREW

Never mix stain removal materials with each other, especially ammonia and chlorine bleach. If it is necessary to use both, make sure one is thoroughly rinsed out before adding the other.

RECIPES FOR SAFE CLEANING PRODUCTS

The following recipes are safe when mixed in the quantities indicated below. The mixing of other household chemicals may be dangerous.

- **All-Purpose Household Cleaner**
  Add 1 teaspoon of any liquid soap and 1 teaspoon of trisodium phosphate (TSP) to 1 quart of warm water. This is a very effective cleaner for many cleaning jobs including countertops and walls. However, try an area of the wall that will not show before using in case your walls are painted with a poor quality water-based flat paint.

- **Chlorine Bleach**
Best to use hydrogen peroxide-based bleach.

- **Degreaser (engines, etc.)**
Best to use a water-based cleaner that is well diluted instead of kerosene, turpentine, or a commercial engine degreaser. These are available in part stores and the label should read "nonflammable," "non-toxic," or "store at temperatures above freezing." These will be water-based products and will do the job.

- **Degreaser (kitchen, grill)**
Add 2 tablespoons of TSP to 1 gallon of hot water or use a non-chlorinated scouring cleanser with a scouring or steel wool pad.

- **Fabric Softener**
Fabrics produced from natural fibers do not need fabric softeners only synthetics.

- **Floor Cleaner**
Vinyl floors: use ½ cup of white vinegar to 1 gallon of warm water.
Wood floors: may be damp moped with a mild liquid soap.

- **Furniture Polish**
Mineral oil may be used, however, most wood surfaces may be cleaned with a damp cloth.

- **Oven Cleaner**
Mix 2 tablespoons of baking soda or TSP in 1 gallon of warm water and scrub with a very fine steel wool pad (0000). Rubber gloves should be worn and the area rinsed well. For difficult baked-on areas, try scrubbing with a pumice stone.
If all of the above fails, try using an oven cleaner that states "no caustic fumes" on the label.

- **Glass Cleaner**
Use 2-3 cup spray bottle with ½ teaspoon of liquid soap, 3 tablespoons of white vinegar and 2 cups of water. If the windows are very dirty, try using more liquid soap.

- **Laundry Detergent**
Use laundry soap in place of the detergents. Washing soda may be used in place of a softener. An alternate would be to use detergents with no added bleaches or softeners. Bleach should be used in moderation when needed.

- **Mildew Remover**
Scrub the area with baking soda or if very stubborn with TSP.

- **Scouring Powder**
Baking soda will work well in most instances.

- **Toilet Bowl Cleaner**
Use a non-chlorinated scouring powder and a stiff brush. To remove hard water deposits, pour white vinegar or a commercial citric acid-based toilet bowl cleaner into the toilet and allow it to sit for several hours or overnight before scrubbing.

NOTE: Washing soda and TSP are caustic and should be kept out of the reach of children.

FABRIC ADVICE:

It is best to know the fiber content in clothing items. If sewn in labels are to be removed, a note should be made as to which item it was removed from. Any durable press or polyester fabric, such as a Dacron, holds soil very well and especially stains. A dry cleaning solvent will work the best. If the stain remains after the first treatment, try once more. If the fabric has been washed or has been placed in a dryer, the stain may never come out.

- Never use chlorine bleach on silk, wool, on Spandex.
- Never remove a stain from leather; take it to dry cleaners to send to an expert.

STAIN REMOVAL FROM WASHABLE FABRICS:

A number of stains can be removed right in your washing machine. Laundry detergents that state that they contain enzymes will provide the best cleaning and stain removal. Enzyme presoak products provide extra cleaning and stain removal for fabrics that may have a more difficult stain. An enzyme detergent or enzyme presoak product should be able to remove the following common stains:

Blood	Gravy	Body soils	Egg
Fruits	Milk	Chocolate	Grass
Cream soups	Baby formula	Puddings	Vegetables
Baby foods	Ice cream	Most food soils	

I WONDER WHERE THE YELLOW WENT

Yellowed fabrics can be restored and even old unknown stains may be removed by first soaking in an enzyme presoak product (Proctor & Gamble has excellent ones) such as Biz and then laundering.

CAN'T PERFORM MAGIC

Remember, even the best enzyme detergent or enzyme presoak product is not capable of removing all types of stains. A number of grease soils and highly colored stains may require special pretreatment before laundering. Since many stains require a variety of different soil removal treatments and techniques, it is important to identify a stain before trying to remove it. A number of stains may actually be set if the wrong method is used.

The following stains will usually be removed with the following recommended methods:

STAIN	METHOD OF REMOVAL
BEVERAGE	Sponge the area with cold water or soak then sponge again. Launder with oxygen bleach and the hottest water that is safe for the fabric.
BLOOD	Soak the fabric in cold water as soon as possible. If the stain persists, soak in warm water with a presoak product before laundering. Try pre-soaking in club soda or milk.

CANDLE WAX The surface wax should be removed with a dull knife. The item should then be placed stain face down on paper towels and then sponge the remaining stain with dry cleaning solvent. Allow to dry and then launder. If traces of color from the wax remains, try soaking it in Biz or an oxygen bleach before laundering again. If the color is still present, try laundering again using chlorine bleach, if the fabric is chlorine bleach safe.

CATSUP\TOMATO PRODUCTS Remove excess with a dull knife, then soak in cold water then launder using the hottest water the fabric will stand.

CHEWING GUM ADHESIVE TAPE RUBBER CEMENT First apply ice to the stain to harden it. Remove excess stain material with a dull knife. Place the item face down on paper towels and sponge with a dry cleaning solvent.

CHOCOLATE\COCOA Soak in cold water then launder with oxygen bleach using the hottest water the fabric will stand.

COFFEE/TEA Best to soak in Biz or an oxygen bleach using the hottest water that is safe for the stained fabric then launder. If the stain persists, try laundering again using chlorine bleach if it is safe to do so.

COSMETICS Dampen stain and rub gently with a white bar soap, then rinse well and launder.

CRAYON If there are only a few spots they can be treated the same as candle wax.
If there are many items that are stained, first wash the items with hot water and laundry soap (e.g. Ivory Snow) and 1 cup of baking soda. If the spots remain, have the clothes dry, cleaned.

DEODORANTS AND ANTIPERSPIRANTS Apply white vinegar, then rub and rinse.
If the stain remains, try saturating the area with rubbing alcohol, rinse, then soak in Biz or an oxygen bleach and launder. If the stain remains wash in chlorine bleach if safe for fabric.

DYE TRANSFER If you have white fabrics that have picked up dye from a colored garment that "bled", try restoring the white by using a fabric color remover. Launder if any of the dye remains using chlorine bleach, if it is safe for the fabric.

EGG/MEAT JUICE Remove excess with a dull knife then soak in cold water. Launder in oxygen bleach in very hot water.

FABRIC SOFTENERS These stains usually result from accidental spills and can be removed by rubbing the area with a piece of cloth moistened with bar soap then launder.

FORMULA Soak in warm water then launder with oxygen bleach and the hottest water that is safe for the fabric.

FRUIT\FRUIT JUICES Soak in cold water before laundering.

GRASS The green area should be sponged with denatured alcohol before washing in very hot water and oxygen bleach.

GREASE STAINS The stained area should be placed face down on paper towels. Dry cleaning solvent should be placed on the back side of the stain and then brushed from the center of the stain to the outer edges using a clean white cloth. Moisten the stain with warm water and rub with bar soap or a mild liquid detergent, then rinse and launder.

GUM Rub with ice and carefully remove the gum with a dull knife before laundering.

INK STAINS For removal of ballpoint stains, place the stain face down on paper towels and sponge the back of the stain with dry cleaning solvent. If there is some ink left, try rubbing the area with moistened bar soap: rinse and then launder.

For any other type of ink stains, just try and remove the stain with a dampened cloth and bar soap, rinse and soak in Biz or an oxygen bleach using very hot water. If the stain won't come out, try using chlorine bleach, if the fabric is safe. Some permanent ink may never be removed.

INK, FELT TIP Rub the area with Fantastic or Mr. Clean, rinse and repeat if necessary. May be impossible to remove.

IODINE Rinse the fabric from the underside with cool water; then soak in a solution of fabric color remover, rinse and then launder.

LIPSTICK The stain should be placed face down on paper towels and then sponged with dry cleaning solvent replacing the paper towels frequently while the color is being removed. Moisten the stain with cool water and then rub with bar soap, rinse and launder.

Hairspray will also remove lipstick.

MILDEW   Fabric should be laundered using chlorine bleach if it is safe for the fabric. If not, try soaking it in oxygen bleach and then launder.

MILK   The fabric should be rinsed in cold water as soon as possible, then washed in cold water using a liquid detergent.

MUSTARD   Moisten stain with cool water, then rub with bar soap, rinse and launder using chlorine bleach, if it is safe for the fabric. If not, soak in Biz or an oxygen detergent using very hot water, then launder. It may take several treatments to remove all of the stain.

Place a few drops of glycerin on your fingers and it will remove mustard.

NAIL POLISH   The fabric stain should be placed face down on paper towels then sponge the back of the stain frequently and repeat until the stain disappears then launder. Never use nail polish remover on fabric, best to have them dry, cleaned.

PAINT   Try to treat the stain while it is still wet. Latex, acrylic, and water, based paints cannot be removed once they have dried. While they are wet: rinse in warm water to flush the paint out then launder.

Oil-based paints can be removed with a solvent that is recommended on the paint can. If it does not give this information, try using turpentine. Rinse and rub with bar soap, then launder.

PERSPIRATION   Moisten the stain and rub with bar soap. Be gentle as perspiration may weaken some fibers, especially silk. Most fabrics should be presoaked in Biz or an enzyme detergent and then laundered in hot water and chlorine bleach, if the fabric is safe.

PERFUME   Same as beverages.

RUST   Never use chlorine bleach on rust, apply a rust stain remover, rinse then launder. You can also use a fabric color remover and then launder or if the stain is really stubborn, try using 1 ounce of oxalic acid crystals (or straight warm rhubarb juice) dissolved in 1 gallon of water, mixed in a plastic container, then rinse and launder.

SCORCH	Soak the fabric in a strong solution of Biz and an oxygen bleach using very hot water if safe for the fabric, then launder. If the scorch remains, it will be necessary to repeat the procedure using chlorine bleach, if the fabric will take it.
SHOE POLISH	Try applying a mixture of 1 part rubbing alcohol and 2 parts of water for colored fabrics and only the straight alcohol for whites.
SUEDE	Rain spots can be removed by lightly rubbing the area with an emery board. If there are grease spots, try using white vinegar or club soda then blot out the stain. Afterwards brush with a suede brush.
TAR	The area should be rubbed with kerosene until all the tar is dissolved, then wash as usual. Test a small area first to be sure it is color, fast.
TOBACCO	Moisten the stain and rub with bar soap, rinse and then launder. If the stain persists, try soaking it in Biz or an oxygen detergent, then launder. As a last resort, use chlorine bleach, if the fabric is safe.
URINE, VOMIT, MUCOUS	Soak the fabric in Biz or an enzyme detergent, launder using chlorine bleach, if safe for the fabric. If not use oxygen bleach with detergent.
WINE/SOFT DRINKS	Soak the fabric with Biz or oxygen bleach using very hot water then launder. Use chlorine bleach if needed and the fabric is safe. Salt works great on red wine before washing.

SOME NATURAL METHODS TO TRY FIRST...

TOTALLY THRIFTY

If you wish to use less detergent and save money, try using slivers of old soaps placed in a sock with the neck tied. Place the sock into the washer and you will use less detergent.

SETTING IT PERMANENTLY

To colorfast a possible problem garment try soaking the colored garment in cold, salty water for 30 minutes before laundering.   ·

DON'T GET STUNG

After washing a piece of clothing with a zipper that has given you problems, try rubbing beeswax on the zipper to resolve the problem and remove any grime that has accumulated.

THE OLD BUBBLE MACHINE

Placing too much soap in the washing machine can cause problems. If this happens, just pour 2 tablespoons of white vinegar or a capful of fabric softener into the machine to neutralize some of the soap.

BEGONE OLD SOAP

When washing clothes, to be sure that all the soap has been removed, try adding 1 cup of white vinegar to the rinse cycle. The vinegar will dissolve the alkalinity in detergents as well as giving the clothes a pleasant fragrance.

THE GREEN, GREEN, GRASS OF HOME

Grass stains will be easily removed with toothpaste, scrub in with a toothbrush before washing. Another method is to rub the stain with molasses and allow it to stand overnight, then wash with regular dish soap by itself. If all else fails, try methyl alcohol, but be sure the color is set, best to try an area that won't show first.

GREASELESS

Spic and Span placed in the washer is a great grease remover, ¼ cup is all that is needed.

WRINKLE REMOVER

To avoid ironing many different types of clothes, just remove them from the dryer the second it stops and fold or hang up immediately.

CATCH THAT COLOR

Washing colored material for the first time may be risky unless you wash it in Epsom salts. One gallon of water to 1 teaspoon is all that is needed. The material will not run.

THE DISAPPEARING ACT

An excellent spot remover can be made using 2 parts of water to 1 part rubbing alcohol.

A DIRTY JOB

To remove difficult dirt, such as collars, mix ⅓ cup of water with ⅓ cup of liquid detergent and ⅓ cup of ammonia. Place the ingredients in a spray bottle. Rubbing shampoo into the area may also work.

LINT MAGNET

To keep corduroy garments from retaining lint, turn them inside out when washing.

HAIRBALLS

To avoid hairballs on acrylic sweaters, turn them inside out when washing them.

ONE OF THE TOUGHEST

Iodine stains can be removed using a mixture of baking soda and water. Allow it to remain on for about 30 minutes rub with mild action.

USE ONLY THE UNSALTED

Butter or margarine will remove tar from clothing, just rub until its gone. The butter is easily removed with any type of spray and wash product.

INKA-KA-DINKA-DOO

Rubbing alcohol or hair spray may remove a number of ink pen stains.

BEWARE OF A TIGHT FIT

If you wash slipcovers, be sure and replace them when they are still damp. They will fit better and will not need to be ironed.

BLOWDRYING

If sweater cuffs are stretched, dip them in hot water and dry with a hairdryer.

A SPOT OF TEA, PERHAPS

Tea stains on tablecloths can be removed with glycerin, try leaving it sit overnight in the solution before washing.

INTO THE FREEZER

Candle wax on tablecloths can be removed by freezing with ice cubes.

REMOVING CANDLE HOLDER WAX

Place the holder in the freezer until the wax has frozen, then chip off.

YUK

Lace doilies should be hand washed in sour milk for the best results.

HOLD THE SHAVING CREAM

If you have a problem with small burrs on sweaters, try using a disposable razor to remove them.

EASY DOES IT

If you are washing a wool garment, be careful not to pull on it. Wool is very weak when wet. Lay the garment on a towel and roll it up and squeeze the excess water out.

NEUTRALIZER

If you have a difficult blood stain, try making a paste of meat tenderizer and cold water. Sponge on the area and allow it to stand for 20-30 minutes. Rinse in cold water, then wash. Hydrogen peroxide may also work.

BATHING STUFFED ANIMALS

To clean stuffed animals that cannot be placed in the washer, just place them in a cloth bag and add baking soda, then shake.

POWDER ME

White flour will clean white gloves, just rub.

A SLIPPERY SUBJECT

Lipstick stains will clean out of clothes by using Vaseline.

A REVIVAL

If you shrink a woolen garment, try soaking it in a hair cream rinse. This will usually make them easy to stretch back into the original size. Another method is to dissolve 1 ounce of Borax in 1 teaspoon of hot water then add it to 1 gallon of warm water. Place the garment in, stretch back to shape then rinse it in 1 gallon of warm water with 2 tablespoons of white vinegar added.

BE STINGY, BE SMART

When you are doing a small wash load, tear the fabric-softening sheet in half for the same results.

A SOLID FACT

To make your own spray starch, purchase 1 bottle of liquid starch concentrate and mix one part of liquid starch to 1 part of water and use a spray bottle.

BUTTON, BUTTON, WHO'S GOT THE BUTTON

If you lose buttons regularly on children's clothing, try sewing them on with dental floss.

TRUE GRIT

If your iron is sticking, try running it over a piece of paper with sprinkled salt on it.

WELL SEASONED CURTAINS

Water stained fabrics should be placed in salt water and soaked until the stain is gone.

BRING IN THE SUB

If you prefer not to use bleach, try substituting 3 tablespoons of hydrogen peroxide to the wash load.

SAVE THE BUTTONS

Always remove buttons before discarding a garment. They may come in handy at a later date.

ATTRACTIVE SALT

Cleaning silk flowers is easy if you place them in a plastic bag with 2 tablespoons of salt and shake vigorously while holding on to the stems. Salt tends to attract the dust.

IRONING SMARTS

When ironing, always iron the fabrics that require a cool temperature first as the iron heats up.

DEW TELL

Mildew on shower curtains can be removed with a mixture of $1/2$ cup bleach, $1/2$ cup powdered detergent, and 1 gallon of water. To prolong the life of shower curtains, add 1 cup of white vinegar to the final rinse.

MAKING COLORS FAST

To prevent jeans from fading (if you want to), soak the jeans in $1/2$ cup of white vinegar and 2 quarts of water for 1 hour before you wash them for the first time.

JEAN SMARTS

Blue jeans should only be washed in cold water then placed in a moderate heat dryer for only 10 minutes. Then they should be placed on a wooden hanger to continue drying.

DOLLAR SAVER

If you would like to save dollars on dry cleaning of wool blankets, try washing them in a mild dishwasher soap on a very gently cycle then air fluff to dry.

NO ONE WILL EVER KNOW

If you scorch a garment, try removing the scorch with cloth that has been dampened with vinegar. Only use a warm iron, not too hot. Cotton scorch marks tend to respond better to peroxide.

INSULATION

A sheet of aluminum foil placed underneath the ironing board cover will allow the heat to be retained for a longer period of time.

BUTTON: BUTTON....

Always remember to place a small amount of clear nail polish in the center of every button on a new garment. This seals the threads and they will last longer.

A SHOCKING SITUATION

A pipe cleaner dipped in white vinegar should be used to clean the holes in the iron after it is completely cool. Make sure it is unplugged.

IF YOU'RE IN A SPOT

Glass cleaner sometimes makes an excellent spot remover if you need something in a hurry. Make sure the fabric is colorfast.

BRIGHTEN-UP

If you want to whiten your whites, try adding a cup of dishwasher detergent to the washer. Even whitens sweat socks.

ANY PENCIL WILL DO

A sticky zipper will respond to a rubbing with a lead pencil. Does an excellent job of lubricating it.

A TEMPORARY SOLUTION

If a button comes off, try reattaching it with the wire from a twist tie.

DON'T SUCK YOUR THUMB

If you use a thimble to sew or sort papers, try wetting your finger before you place the thimble on. This creates suction and holds the thimble on.

A SEALER

When you wash you sneakers, spray them with a spray starch to help them resist becoming soiled.

DIRTY BOTTOM

If the bottom of the iron gets dirty, just clean it with a steel wool soap pad. If you want to make it shiny again, just run a piece of waxed paper over it.

RUSTADE

Rust marks on clothing can be removed with lemon juice and a small amount of salt easily rubbed in and then allowed to sit in the sun for 2 hours.

A LITTLE BUBBLY

Red wine can be removed from a tablecloth by wetting the area with club soda and allowing it to stand for 20 minutes before washing.

AND AWAY WE GO

To dry the insides of shoes or sneakers, try placing the blower end of the vacuum hose inside.

A TRIPPER-UPPER

If you have problems with your shoelaces becoming undone, just dampen them before tying them.

A WORD OF CAUTION

Silk clothing should be hand washed using cool water with Ivory liquid soap. When you rinse, try adding a small amount of lanolin to help preserve the material. Always drip dry, never place the garment in the dryer then iron using a soft piece of cloth over the garment.

SHAPE-UP, AND DON'T LOSE YOUR COLOR

Cold water should always be used in the rinse cycle to help the clothes retain their shape and color.

ASSORTED HINTS AND TIPS

www.ci.nyc.us/html/doh/htm/lead/leatw.html

www.brazosport.cc.tx.us/~hpekar/nate/facts/factsma

DECAL BEGONE

www.thefunplace.com/house/tips/clean.html

COVER UP

www.alkaseltzer.com

www.wackyuses.com/alkaseltzer.html

GET THE STINK OUT OF GASOLINE

www.makestuff.com/grandpa.html

STREAKER

www.geocities.com/PicketFence/1990/tips.html

PASS ME THE PEANUT BUTTER, HOLD THE HAIR

www.wackuses.com/jelly.html

LEATHER REVIVAL

www.homeimages.com/household/cleaning.htm

ODOR EATERS

www.geocities.com/PicketFence/1990/tips.html

ON A CLEAR DAY

www.ourhousetv.com/clean.html

A SALAD SOLUTION

www.fac.unc.edu/WasteReduction/cleaning.html

http://members.aol.com/stephndon/tips.htm

LEMON TREE

www.mosdesign.com/watkins/tips2.html

GLUE

www.thefunplace.com/house/tips/clean.html

A GIRL'S BEST FRIEND

www.geocities.gom/Heartland/Village/8707/Recipies2.html

EXTINGUISHING THE OLD FLAME

www.lancealotta.com/lisa/house.html

A POPPER OUTER

http://members.tripod.com/~tassiedevil/coke.htm

NEUTRALIZE ME

www.tased.edu.au/tasonline/tech/11-3-1.htm

SMILE

www.makestuff.com/vinegar.html

RING AROUND THE TABLE

www.lancealotta.com/lisa/house.html

A NUTTY SOLUTION

http://members.xoom.com/FrugalLiving/tips9.html

IT REALLY HITS THE SPOT

http://thefamilyvoice.freeservers.com/tips.html

GREASE CUTTER

www.engineering.ucsb.edu/~tbmaddux/env/cleaners.html

SPRINKLE, SPRINKLE

www.interlution.com/quicktips/R0939.htm

REMOVING ODORS

http://members.aol.com/Grumpy2nAM/household2.htm

MEASURING UP

www.inlandempireonline.com/food/stories/howtomeasure

SMART MOVE

www.foodscience.afisc.csro.au/migpac.htm

DON'T BURST YOUR BUBBLE

http://bubbles.org/solutions

www.recipexchange.com/recipexchange_cfmfiles/Recipes.cfm/2850

SAVES ON THE WASHING

www.brazosport.cc.tx.us/~hpekar/nate/facts/factsma

REAL MILK SHAKE

www.survivalcity.com/survival-city/powderedmilk.htlm

COMING UNGLUED

www.wanderers2.com/rose/easy.html

SALVAGE JOB

http://members.aol.com/stephndon/tips.html

CRUMMY SOLUTION

www.wanderers2.com/rose/easy.html

SUMMERTIME

http://answersleuth.com/food/seasoning.id.shtml

EATABLE CANDLE HOLDER

www.w.mall.com/wjpierman/simple_hints1.html

SLICK IDEA

http://members.xoom.com/FrugalLiving/tips9.html

WORKS LIKE MAGIC

www.lancellotta.com/lisa/house.html

GETTING IN SHAPE

www.uwex.edu/ces/flp/speacialists/ingham/jul98.html

COMING UNGLUED

www.mall.com/wjpierman/simple_hints1.html

THRIFTY IDEA

www.lancellotta.com/lisa/house.html

HUNDREDS OF YEARS OLD

www.chatlink.com/~herbseed/feverfew.html

CAN PROTECTION

http://surf.tstc.edu/~trodriguez/#tips

NO NIPPING, IT'S POISON

www.pitstop.co.nz/hints_tips.html

TRY, SODIUM PHOSPHATE

www.sdearthtimes.com/et0496/et0496s2.html

RUB-A-DUB-DUB

www.wackyuses.com/wesson.html

TO THE SEAT OF THE PROBLEM

www.wanderers2.com/rose/easy.html

PERSONAL GROOMING FACTS

www.armhammer.com
www.homestead.com/20uses/bakingsoda.html
http://burn.ucsd.edu/remedies/remedies.html
www.homeimages.com/household/cleaning.htm
www.lancellotta.com/lisa/beauty_tips.html
www.cis.ohio-state.edu/hypertext/faq/usenet-faqs/html/caffeine-faq/faq.html

THIS WILL SNAP YOU AWAKE INSTANTLY
www.thefunplace.com/house/tips/hhtips.html

TASTES GOOD TOO
http://maxpages.com/goddessmegan/Beauty_Tips_for_everyone

NEW USE FOR BREAKFAST FOOD
http://maxpages.com/livingbetter

ODE DE REFRIGERATOR
www.thefunplace.com/house/tips/beauty.html

GREAT FOR HALLOWEEN
http://thirdagemedia.com/news/archive/981214-02.html

WHY DIDN'T I THINK OF THAT
www.wackyuses.com/jelly.html

FRUIT-PASTE
www.rowan.edu/mars/clubs/gaia/lips.html

A LITTLE DAB WILL DO YA
www.stretcher.com/stories/961202d.htm http://maxpages.com/living

A PASTY
http://primarycare.medscape.com/CPG/ClinReviews/1998/vo8

SHAMPOO AWAY
http://members.aol.com/Grumpy2nAm/household2.htm

A LITTLE ACID GOES A LONG WAY
www.cyber-north.com/tipnet/vinegar.html

THE EYES HAVE IT
www.thirdage.com/news/archive/981214-02.html

PERFUME HOLDER
www.homestead.com/20uses/perfume.html

SKINADE
www.chandigarhcity.com/temp/tip.html

BALANCING ACT
http://ww2.nitco.com./users/tuscan/page18.htm

BEING THRIFTY
www.cyber-north.com/tipnet/vinegar.html

SWEET GRIT
www.suresite.com/or/g/garden

A LITTLE SQUIRT
www.lancellotta.com/lisa/beauty_tips.html

EVERYDAY HOUSEHOLD PRODUCTS

HOW CAN I MAKE AN EFFECTIVE GROUT CLEANER?
www.wizardofformulas.com

SHOULD WE USE A PHOSPHATE DETERGENT?
www.planetinc.com

WHAT DO FABRIC SOFTENERS ACTUALLY DO?
www.immuneweb.org/articles/fabricsofteners.html

WHAT CAUSES THE RINGS ON TOILET BOWLS?
www.fiaaz.net/SanitarySupply/82110010.htm

WHAT IS SOAP MADE OUT OF?
www.compusmart.ab.ca/sbra/lynden
www.craftcave.com

HOW IS TALLOW PRODUCED?
http://candleandsoap.about.com/msubsoapinstr.htm

WHY DOES IVORY SOAP FLOAT?
www.madsci.com
www.ideafinder.com/facts/story/story030.htm

IS COLD CREAM THE SAME AS CLEANSING CREAM?
www.craftmall.com

ARE SHAMPOOS SIMILAR TO LIQUID DISH SOAP?
www.bleakman.com/soap/soap.html

HOW DOES A LIQUID HAIR REMOVER WORK?

www.omline.net/igiahairplaza.htm

WHAT IS TOOTHPASTE COMPOSED OF?

www.wholepop.com/features/oralhgn/truth.html

WHAT IS VASELINE MADE OUT OF?

http://home.nycap.rr.com/useless/vaseline/vaseline.html

PAIN RELIEVERS?

http://dem0nmac.mgh.harvard.edu/forum/PorphyriaF/1.23.991
www.market.econ.vanderbilt.edu/ba250/fall98/Tylenol
www.mothernature.com/articles/HAAS/DMSO/ARTICLE1.stm
http://lycos.infoplease.com/cee5/CEO30785.html

ARE OVEN CLEANERS DANGEROUS?

www.adam.com/encyclopedia/002800sym.htm

HOW DOES ANTIFREEZE WORK

www.coolants.com
www.aftermarketworld.com/cm/cm59730.htm

CAN COLA REALLY CLEAN MY CAR BATTERY?

www.wackyuses.com/coke.html

WHAT IS THE DIFFERENCE BETWEEN A CAR POLISH AND A WAX?

www.personalautodetail.com/QAIndex.htm

WHAT IS THE DIFFERENCE BETWEEN CEMENT AND CONCRETE?

www.cemstone.com/questions/questions.htm#cement
www.lime.co.nz/EducationalArea

WHAT MAKES A DISINFECTANT DIFFERENT FROM AN ANTISEPTIC?

www.steamatic-cr.com/bioclean/PRINCIPLES.html

WHAT HAPPENS WHEN YOU HAVE YOUR HAIR STRAIGHTENED?

www.livingmall.com/hair/relaxers.html

DO I NEED A SPECIAL DETERGENT FOR COLD WATER WASHING?

www.sdahq.org/sdalatest/html/laundry_tips.html

DO DRY BLEACHES WORK BETTER THAN LIQUID BLEACHES?
www.fwkc.com/encyclopidia/low/articles/b/b00300168

ARE THE EXPENSIVE BATHTUB CLEANERS REALLY NECESSARY?
www.zinsser.com/press/1999/mildew_tips.html

DO ACNE MEDICATIONS WORK?
www.thiele.fptoday.com/ta/acnehome.htm

DOES COLA REALLY CONTROL NAUSEA AND VOMITING?
http://managedcare.medscape.com/SMA/SMJ/1999/v92.n02/smj9

HOW DOES BAKING SODA REMOVE ODORS?
www.prc.org/bakings.html

DO WINDSHIELD DEICERS REALLY WORK?
www.snomelt.com

WHAT CAN I USE TO CLEAN SILVERSTONE AND TEFLON POTS?
www.lancellotta.com/lisa/house.html

HOW CAN I UNCLOG A DRAIN USING INGREDIENTS AROUND THE KITCHEN
www.brazosport.cc.tx.us/~hpekar/nate/facts/factsma

ALL CHOPSTICKS ARE NOT THE SAME
www.ogasawara-ryu.com/en/taboo.html

WHAT IS AN EASY METHOD OF OVEN CLEANING
www.cepinc.com/N_bbq.htm

HOME AND GARDEN TIPS

MODERATION, A MUST
www.wackuses.com/jelly.html

THE DISAPPEARING ACT
www.shadesofcolor.com/tips.htm

I CAN SEE A RAINBOW
www.makestuff.com/pinecones.html

REAL SHARPIE
www.gracefulbee.com/tipsheet/tip028.htm

DON'T GET ZAPPED
http://cgi.pathfinder.com/drweil/qa_answer/0%2c3189%2c5%2

SNOW SLIDE
www.wanderers2.com/rose/easy.html

SEEING THE LIGHT
www.backwoodshome.com/articles/lindsey43.html

SPRINKLE, SPRINKLE, LITTLE SALT
www.interlution.com/quicktips/r0939.htm

A SWEETER YULE
www.fun.co.nz/ventech/apexpines/christmas_info/tre
www.kwtv.com/news/fixit/chtrees.htm

NATURAL FERTILIZERS

www.apex.net.au/~jokers/handyhints.htm

SMOOTHIE

http://homes.southjersey.com/wallpaper6.cfm

HOP, SCOTCH

www.wanderers2.com/rose/easy.html

COLA WORKS GREAT TOO

http://members.tripod.com/~tassiedevil/coke.htm

FOR SAFETY'S SAKE

www.psghs.edu/pubtips/W/YuletideHolidaySafety.htm

ELECTRICIANS TRICK

http://members.aol.com/Grumpy2nAM/household2.htm

GLUB, GLUB

www.wanderers2.com/rose/easy.html

WEED-A-WAY

www.surfsouth.com/~striix/nat.html

HOW DRY I AM

www.gardenguides.com

GETTING POTTED

www.wackuses.com/mrcoffee.html

www.geocities.com/Heartland/Park/1873/gardentip

ESPECIALLY HARD ROCK ONES

www.apex.net.au/~jokers/handyhints.htm

GETTING A LEG UP

www.apex.net.au/~jokers/handyhints.htm

FOUR EYES

http://doityourself.com/paint/index.htm

PAM TO THE RESCUE

www.thefunplace.com/house/tips/clean.html

HANDY RULER

www.doitbestcorp.com/projects/Articles/864310543

A CHILLING SOLUTION

www.detriotnews.com/homestyl/9805/09/tipshomegarden

AND A LONNNNG EXTENSION CORD

http://homearts.com/helpers/homecare/hrefrof1.htm

PAINT HOLDERS

www.maycom.com/hints1.html

KEEPING GREASE IN ITS PLACE

http://homes.southjersey.com/wallpaper6.cfm

SKIN TIP

http://doityourself.com/paint/index.htm

GETTING FIT AND STAYING FIT

METABOLISM, WHAT IS IT?
http://metabolism.use-webmd.com
www.biotech.icmb.utexas.edu/pages/science/metabolism.html

THE ENERGY BALANCE
http://ns.ulaval.ca/vrr/rech/Proj/56291.html
http://nutrition.ps.edu/undergrad/courses/nutr25/nutr25

EXERCISE
www.superslow.com
http://ecercise.health.net
http://exerciseroutines.fitpeople.com

BENEFITS OF EXERCISE
www.benefits

SMOKING
www.kib.ki.se/ki/diss/970822/jens.html

AEROBICS AND FITNESS
www.cooperinst.org

FAST AND SLOW TWITCH MUSCLE FIBERS
http://k-2.stanford.edu/~thu/MusclePages/skeletal_athleti

JUST FOR THE FUN OF IT

HOME FITNESS EQUIPMENT

Rowing Machines

www.bodytrends.com

www.mylifepath.com/topic/644

Treadmills

http://treadmills.searchassistance.com

Mini-Trampolines

www.trampolinesusa.com

Stationary Bike (Ergometer)

www.healthwave.com

Multi-Gyms

www.leisurefitness.com

www.atlanticfitness.com

FITNESS FACTS:

INJURIES AND PREVENTION

Blisters

http://footblisters.home-webmd.com

Arch Conditions

www.orthodynamics.com

Sprained Ankle

www.coolrunning.com

www.np.ac.sq/~gom/images/sprained.htm

Knee Problem

www.kneeandhips.com/knee/kneesym.htm

Lower Back Pain

www.lowerbackpain.health-webmd.com

www.pgaonline.com/Fitness/faqa4.html

Muscle Soreness

www.musclesoreness.health-asimba.com

OSide Stitch

www.runnersworld.com/injuries/stitch.html

www.medicaltalk.com/6310.html

Achilles Tendon Rupture
www.fwkc.com/encyclopedia/low/articles/a/a00100019

Achilles Tendon Bursitis and Tendinitis
http://achillestendoninjuries.browse-women.com

Shin Splints
www.doitsports.com

www.healthyideas.com/weight/gym/980128.gym.html

WALKING NECESSARY TO WALK OFF COMMON SNACK FOODS
www.nih.gov/news/stepbystep/calories.htm

VITAMINS, ANTIOXIDANTS & MORE

SUPPLEMENTS

www.sterolin2000.com

www.healthchoice.net/tips/why_take_vits.html

DIGESTIVE ENZYMES

www.thefamilysolution.com

LOSS OF NUTRIENT AVAILABILITY IN FOODS

SMOKING AND VITAMIN C

www.sci.tamucc.edu/stjs/abstracts/clepper.html

DAIRY PRODUCT INTOLERANCE

www.rxmed.com/monographs/lactaid.html

HORMONAL CHANGES

www.thefamilysolution.com

www.sterolin2000.com

HIGH PROTEIN INTAKE = DANGER

www.afpafitness.com/Protein2.htm

http://health.iafrica.com/dietonline/dietga/lifestyle/high

VITAMIN ROBBERS

SUPPLEMENTS FOR THE NEW MILLENNIUM

STEROLS/STEROLINS

www.sterolin2000.com

PHYTOCHEMICALS

www.sterolin2000.com

www.phys.com/b_nutrition/03encyclopedia/02terms/p

www.ambrosiaherbals.com/phyto.html

PHYTOCHEMICALS IN FRUITS, VEGETABLES AND HERBS

http://207.153.213.131/

www.berkeley.edu

www.sciencedaily.com

www.ag.uiuc.edu/~stratsoy/experts/abs17.html

www.tagnet.org/abstracts/search/v5/n3/v5n31.htm

www.nalusda.gov/fnic/etex/000102.htm

www.floridachemical.com/photos.html

www.nalusda.gov/ttic/tektran/data/000007/29/000007

www.red-raspberry.com/pages/ellagic

www.phys.com/b_nutrition/03encyclopedia/02terms/p/

www.confex.com/ift/99annual/abstracts/4407.htm

www.kcweb.com/herb/vit_bc.htm

www.aegis.com/pubs/gmhc/1993/GM071115.html

www.ag.uiuc.edu/~ffh/abstracts/Abstracts47.html

www.teatalk.com

www.nutritionsciencenews.com/NSN_backs/Sep_96/brie

www.flaxseedbodywarmers.com/links

www.ag.uiuc.edu/~ffh/abstracts/Abstracts47.html

www.lifeservices.com/products/lutein.cfm

www.oceanspray.com

http://agrochem.var/fgov.be/anthocyanins.htm

www.fwkc.com/encyclopedia/low/articles/s/s02300049

http://web.net-link.net/preparedfoods/1999/9901/9901Development.htm

www.ifrn.bbsrc.ac.uk

www.ag.uiuc.edu/~ff/abstracts/Abstracts41.html

PROANTHOCYANIDIN (PAC)

www.sterolin2000.com

www.accesscom.com/~abbey/wvap/grapeseed.html

www.mothernature.com/ency/Supp/Proanthocyanidin.asp

CAROTENOIDS

www.essential.org/cspi/nah/3_99/antioxidant.htm

www.atkins.com/HH/Carotene.htm

MAJOR CAROTENOIDS

www.smartbasic.com/glos.herbs/broccoli.html

http://webtutor.tamu.edu/students/lin/project/Lycopene.html

CAROTENOID-ENHANCED VEGETABLES

www.foodfuture.org.uk/ffoods2.htm

CO-ENZYME Q10 (ubiquinone)

www.lougehrigsdisease.net/als_pages/Ask%20the%20ph

www.naturalconnections.com/Cog101.poic.htm

SHARK CARTILAGE

www.c4yourself.com/health-tips/sharkcartilage.shtml

http://mel.lib.mi.us/health/health-alternative-shark.html

DHEA (dehydroepiandrosterone)

www.naples.net/~nfn03605/

www.teleport.com/~genel/dhea.html

ANTIOXIDANT ENZYMES

Superoxide Dismutase (SOD)

www.mothernature.com/ency/Diet/Antioxidants.asp

Glutathione Peroxidase (GP)

www.smartbasic.com/glos.aminos/gluthione.glos.html

Methionine Reductase (MR)

http://link.springer-ny.com/links/service/journals/00018/b

CHLORELLA

www.sunchlorella.net/chlorellaindetail.htm

www.heartsources.com/food/chlorella/chlorella.htm

NEW TEST FOR ANTIOXIDANT LEVELS IN FOODS

www.ars.usda.gov

FARMERS WILL BE WORKING PHARMACISTS

http://web.net-link.net/preparedfoods/1998/9807/9807funcfood2.htm
www.ext.vt.edu/news/periodicals/foods/products/98nov-11.html
www.ifrn.bbsrc.ac.uk
www.ag.uiuc.edu/~ff/abstracts/Abstracts41.html

SOY TO FIGHT HEART DISEASE

www.uiuc.edu
www.ars.usda.gov/is/np/fnrb/fnrb498.htm
www.sciencedaily.com/releases/1999/02/990204081347.htm

http://web.net-link.net/preparedfoods/1999/9904/9904japan.htm
http://web.net-link.net/preparedfoods/1999/9901/9901newprod.htm

WEIGHT CONTROL

http://web.net-link.net/preparedfoods/1999/9903/9903newprod.htm
http://whyfiles.news.wisc.edu/051fat_fixes/cla.html
http://jacksonville.com/tu-online/stories/041798/bus_1c8DietS.html

SEA SICKNESS

http://bevnet.com/reviews/sailorsdelight/index.asp

VITAMIN F

www.healthy.net

ARTERY DISEASES

http://web.net-link.net/preparedfoods/1999/9904/9904japan.htm

www.ifrn.bbsrc.ac.uk
www.ag.uiuc.edu/~ff/abstracts/Abstracts41.html
www.ifrn.bbsrc.ac.uk
www.ag.uiuc.edu/~ff/abstracts/Abstracts41.html

LIQUID NUTRITIONAL PRODUCTS

DIET DRINKS

www.thefamilysolution.com
www.inprotv.com/nutrition.htm
www.formyou3.com
www.naturesbest.com/html/body_beverages.html
www.slim4life.com/basic.html

COLLOIDAL MINERALS

www.colloidalmineral.com
www.healthplusdirect.com/c.htm
www.reach4life.com/colloidalsilver.html

LIQUID VITAMINS

www.thefamilysolution.com
www.thefamilysolution.com
www.sterolin2000.com

LIQUID NUTRITIONAL INFORMATION

http://herbsnow.com/chlorophyll.htm
www.powersupplements.com/creatine.htm

HOW STABLE ARE VITAMINS IN BEVERAGES?

www.pdlab.com/vitstabx.htm

SPORTS DRINKS

www.aqaloe.com/drinks.html
http://bevnet.com/reviews/powerade/index.asp
http://bevnet.com/reviews/battery/index.asp
www.mayohealth.org/mayo/9510/htm/energyge.htm
www.guts.ca/guts3.htm
www.bevnet.com
www.bevnet.com/reviews/ginspring/index.asp
www.spluk.com/powerup.htm
www.bevnet.com

www.bevnet.com
http://bevnet.com/reviews/bluepig/
http://bevnet.com/reviews/xtc/index.asp

NATURAL LIQUID SPRAYS

www.thefamilysolution.com
www.steroli2000.com
www.wizardofformulas.com

GENERAL NUTRITIONAL DRINKS

www.mayohealth.org/mayo/9607/htm/drnk_1sb.htm
http://web.net-link.net/preparedfoods/1999/9903/9903newprod.htm

PETS, INSECTS AND PESKY CRITTERS

www.montanasky.net/vegepet/
www.ecwa.asn.au/info/altpest.html#ants
www.wpvq.com/wtipfeeddog.htm
http://192.225.33.129/magazine/foods/body/factoids/index.html
www.homestead.com/homeremedies/pest.html
www.ecwa.asn.au/info/altpest.html
www.menagerie.on.ca/02-99/quest.html
www.geocities.com/Heartland/Park/1873/gardentip
www.oakandassociates.com/~melissk/pestcont.html#flies
www.bosbbb.org/lit/0068.htm
www.bosbbb.org/lit/0068.htm
www.namyco.org/educ/c-nam.htm

MOSQUITOES

www.oakandassociates.com/~melissk/pestcont.html
www.fwkc.com/encyclopedia/low/articles/c/c00500064

MOTH TRAPPER

www.users.zenet.co.uk/rjseago/mtrap.htm
www.finegardening.com/th/features/fitandfabric/21moths.htm
www.attra.org/attra-pub/baksoda.html

www.planetpets.simplenet.com/grdntips14.htm

SNAIL

http://telegraph.hoosiertimes.com/stories/1998/08/05/lifestyle

RODENT REPELLER #1

www.thefunplace.com/house/tips/hhtips.html

MICE

www.yahooligans.com/content/kalalmanac/lawright/la
www.ecwa.asn.au/info/altpest.html#rats&mice

RODENT REPELLER #2

www.orcbs.msu.edu/AWARE/pamphlets/auto/oil.html

www.homestead.com/homeremedies/pest.html
www.thefunplace.com/house/tips/hhtips.html
http://telegraph.hoosiertimes.com/stories/1998/08/05/lifestyle
www.9online.com/news/fixit/critters.htm
www.mayohealth.org/mayo/9712/htm/2nd_op1.htm

CARPENTER ANTS & TERMITES

www.tipztime.com/area/bugtipz/ants.html

WEEVIL

www.ecwa.asn.au/info/altpest.html

FLEAS

www.tipztime.com/area/bugtipz/fleas.html
www.ecwa.asn.au/info/altpest.html#fleas

ROACHES

www.hints-n-tips.com/household.htm
http://thefamilyvoice.freeservers.com/tips.html

www.geocities.com/Heartland/Park/1873/gardentip

www.healthyforlife.org/summernews/tips.html
http://telegraph.hoosiertimes.com/stories/1998/08/05/lifestyle

MOSQUITOES

www.tipztime.com/area/bugtipz/gnatsmosquitoes.html
www.makestuff.com/grandpa.html
www.tipztime.com/area/bugtipz/gnatsmosquitos.html

WRIGGLERS

http://plaza.powersurfr.com/bw/bestoffinchlovers/fl-nu-me

SQUIRREL

www.tipztime.com/area/bugtipz/squirrels.html

STAINS BEGONE

GENERAL RULES TO REMOVE STAINS

http://spectre.ag.uiuc.edu/~robsond/solutions/consumer/do
www.oznet.ksu.edu/
www.bae.ncsu.edu/bae/programs/extension/publicat/w
http://ext.msstate.edu/pubs/pub1400.htm
www.lancelotta.com/lisa/house.html
www.mcrecord.com/MCR_Editorial/98july/Gen980701
http://ca.yahoo.com/Recreation/Home_and_Garden/Stain-Removal

STAIN REMOVAL PRODUCTS

www.rainbowwintl.com/stain.htm

CHEMICAL ALERT

www.ext.msstate.edu/pubs/is1436.htm

www.agschool.fusc.peachnet.edu/html/publications/Telet
www.textileaffairs.com/stains.htm

www.fabriclink.com/holidaystain.html

CONTAINER SMARTS

www.pp.okstate.edu/ehs/links/home.htm
www.uetigers.stier.org/library/mrktplchemhousehold
www.2.msstate.edu/~gmmy/chemistry/general.html
www.chem.utah.edu/chemistry/classes/labs/safety/sa
www.bockstanz.com/Safety%20Library/SL-Bleach.h1
www.bae.ncsu.edu/bae/programs/extension/publicat/w

All-Purpose Household Cleaner
www.wizardofformulas.com
Degreaser (engines, etc.)
www.wizardofformulas.com
Fabric Softener
www.wizardofformulas.com
Furniture Polish
www.wizardofformulas.com
Oven Cleaner
www.wizardofformulas.com
Laundry Detergent
www.wizardofformulas.com
Toilet Bowl Cleaner
www.wizardofformulas.com
http://ex.msstate.edu/pubs/is1436.htm
www.lalc.k12.ca.us/target/units/recycle/recipes.html

FABRIC ADVICE:
www.tide.com/tipsTimeSavers/fabricCare.html

STAIN REMOVAL FROM WASHABLE FABRICS:
www.pg.com/schooldays/cleaning/24301.htm
www.fabriclink.com/holidaystain2.htm#yellowing
www.visatablelinen.com/custom.htm
www.penpages.psu.edu/penpages_reference/28602/2860

STAIN — METHOD OF REMOVAL

BEVERAGE
www.countrysave.com/stains.htm

BLOOD
www.aliceville.com/stains.htm

CANDLE WAX
http://Doit

CHOCOLATE\COCOA
www.exnet.iastate.edu/Pages/communications/holiday/stain.html

COFFEE/TEA

www.aliceville.com/stains.htm

COSMETICS

www.webpages.com/plush/cosmetics.html

CRAYON

www.cybermom.com/bin/netforum/broomchat/a.cgi/8—1.20.1.13

DEODORANTS AND ANTIPERSPIRANTS

www.heloise.com/topten.html

DYE TRANSFER

www.countysave.com/stains.htm

EGG/MEAT JUICE

http://doit

FABRIC SOFTENERS

www.countysave.com/stains.htm

FORMULA

www.momsonline.com/asafamily/article.asp?key=M0440903

GRASS

http://spectre.ag.uiuc.edu/~robson/solutions/consumer/d

GREASE STAINS

www.webpages.com/plush/grease.html

GUM

http://kwtv.com/news/fixit/mf720.htm

INK, FELT TIP

www.exnet.iastate.edu/Pages/communications/holiday/stain.html

IODINE

http://doityourself.com/clean/iodine.htm

LIPSTICK

www.toessel.com/~alaina/whatces/stains/stains.html

MILDEW

http://doityouself.com/clean/moldandmildew.htm

MUSTARD

www.teamfisher.com/mainten/carpet/page2.html

NAIL POLISH

http://aagschool.fusc.peachnet.edu/html/publications/telet

PAINT

www.countrysave.com/stains.htm

PERSPIRATION

www.toessel.com/~whatces/stains/stains.html

PERFUME

www.countrysave.com/stains.htm

RUST

www.aliceville.com/stains.htm

SCORCH

www.aliceville.com/stains.htm

SHOE POLISH

www.webpages.com/plush/shoe.html

TAR

www.sheepusa.org/woolspot.htm

TOBACCO

www.countrysave.com/stains.htm

URINE, VOMIT

http://doityourself.com/clean/urine.htm

SOME NATURAL METHODS TO TRY FIRST...

SETTING IT PERMANENTLY

www.newswest.com/svherald/daily/97/mar/05/C3-austi

THE OLD BUBBLE MACHINE

www.doityourself.com/clean/laundrycleaners.htm

BEGONE OLD SOAP

www.doityourself.com/clean/laundrycleaners.htm

THE GREEN, GREEN, GRASS OF HOME

www.textileaffairs.com/stains.htm

WRINKLE REMOVER

www.textileaffairs.com/stains.htm

www.geocities.com/Heartland/Park/1873/laundrytips.htm

CATCH THAT COLOR

http://members.aol.com/Grumpy2nAM/household2.htm

A DIRTY JOB

www.thefunplace.com/house/tips/clean.html

http://ext.msstate.edu/pubs/pub1400.htm

LINT MAGNET

www.lancellotta.com/lisa/house.html

HAIRBALLS

www.wanderers2.com/rose/easy.html

INKA-KA-DINKA-DOO

www.fabriclink.com/holidaystain.html#dyestains

www.geocities.com/Wellesley/Veranda/8009/household

INTO THE FREEZER

http://asia.yahoo.com/Recreation/Home_and_Garden/Stain-Rem

HOLD THE SHAVING CREAM

http://www.printlee.com/nextdim/winter97/g_and_a.htm

NEUTRALIZER

www.geocities.com/PicketFence/1990/tips.html

www.geocities.com/Wellesley/Veranda/8009/hints2

A SLIPPERY SUBJECT

www.wackuses.com/jelly.html

www.suite101.com/article.cfm/house_tips/24370

A SOLID FACT

www.doityourself.com/clean/laundrycleaners.htm

TRUE GRIT

www.wanderers2.com/rose/easy.html

WELL SEASONED CURTAINS

www.geocities.com/PicketFence/1990/tips.html

BRING IN THE SUB

www.geocities.com/Heartland/Park/1873

SAVE THE BUTTONS

www.wanderers2.com/rose/easy.html

ATTRACTIVE SALT

http://members.aol.com/Grumpy2nAM/household2.htm

DEW TELL

www.pioneerthinking.com/bathroom.html

www.thefunplace.com/house/tips/clean.html

JEAN SMARTS

www.printlee.com/nextdim/winter97/tips.htm

DOLLAR SAVER

www.pioneerthinking.com/laundry.html

NO ONE WILL EVER KNOW

www.fabriclink.com/holidaystain2.html

BUTTON: BUTTON....

www.thefunplace.com/house/tips/hhtips.html

IF YOU'RE IN A SPOT

http://members.aol.com/Grumpy2nAM/household2.htm

BRIGHTEN-UP

www.momsonline.com/homespace/cleansweep/article.as

ANY PENCIL WILL DO

www.lacellotta.com/lisa/beautytips.html

A SEALER

www.sneakers-nation.com/care.html

RUSTADE

www.fabriclink.com/holidaystain2.html

A LITTLE BUBBLY

www.wackyuses.com/canadadry.html

A TRIPPER-UPPER

http://www.geocities.com/Heartland/Park/1873

A WORD OF CAUTION

www.ivory.com/ivoryliquid/liq_faqs.html

SHAPE-UP, AND DON'T LOSE YOUR COLOR

www.oznet.ksu.edu/ctid/timely%20topics/effects.htm
http://stains.com/tipsTimeSavers/fabricCare.html